RADIO PLAYS
for CHILDREN

RADIO PLAYS
for CHILDREN

Selected and Arranged by

KATHERINE WILLIAMS WATSON

Head Children's Department,
Denver Public Library

THE H. W. WILSON COMPANY
NEW YORK   1947

Acknowledgments

Acknowledgment is gratefully made to the following for permission to use the copyright material contained in this book; permission to use such material in radio or other productions must be obtained from publishers or agents as specified below.

Robert L. Grimes, for The BAKER'S TOP-HAT BUNNY, adapted from the *Baker's Top-Hat Bunny* by Robert L. Grimes. Copyright, 1942, by *Jack and Jill Magazine*. May be used non-commercially without payment of royalty; for other use, apply to Katherine Williams Watson.

The Macmillan Company, for BECKY'S THANKSGIVING TURKEY, adapted from *Becky Landers; Frontier Warrior* by Constance Lindsay Skinner. Copyright, 1926, by The Macmillan Company. All rights reserved. May not be reproduced in any form, or performed publicly or broadcast, except by written permission of The Macmillan Company.

The Viking Press, for BLUE WILLOW, adapted from *Blue Willow* by Doris Gates. Copyright, 1940, by Doris Gates. Used by special arrangement with The Viking Press, Inc. All rights reserved. May not be reproduced in any form, or performed publicly or broadcast, except by written permission of The Viking Press, 18 East 48th Street, New York, N.Y.

The Macmillan Company, for BUCKAROO, adapted from *Buckaroo* by Fjeril Hess. Copyright, 1931, by The Macmillan Company. All rights reserved. May not be reproduced in any form, or performed publicly or broadcast, except by written permission of The Macmillan Company.

Houghton Mifflin Company, for A CANDLE IN THE MIST, adapted from *A Candle in the Mist* by Florence Crannell Means. Copyright, 1931, by Florence C. Means. May not be reproduced in any form, or performed publicly or broadcast, except by written permission of Houghton Mifflin Company.

Henry Holt and Company, for THE CHRISTMAS MONKS, adapted from a dramatization of a story by Mary E. Wilkins Freeman by Elsie Hobart Carter in *Christmas Candles*. Copyright, 1915, by

Dedicated to my librarian

MALCOLM GLENN WYER

and to the staff of the
Denver Public Library

Preface

Julia Sauer in her preface to *Radio Roads to Reading* says, "If we believe in books and their power to bring pleasure and profit into children's lives, books must be advertised more strenuously than ever, and they must be advertised in new ways."

Feeling this need, the Children's Department of the Denver Public Library sponsored a children's radio program called "Once Upon A Time" over KOA, a National Broadcasting Company station, for six years.

The plays in this book are an outgrowth of this program. These are dramatizations for radio of children's books and stories. Six of these plays were presented on our children's program. After the scripts were written, different schools were asked to be responsible for their production; other organizations like the Boy Scouts, Girl Scouts and Camp Fire Girls also participated.

For the convenience of busy teachers and librarians, the plays have been arranged by subject and by grade, and range from simple plays for the third grade to the more difficult for the upper grades. While the plays are primarily for radio programs for children, they can also be used in schools. If one wishes to carry out the idea of radio, this could be arranged by simply pretending to have a real microphone. Use a cardboard cut-out or tin-can dummy microphone mounted on a broomstick or bridge lamp. The announcer reads the opening announcement and the description of the scenes in the clear fashion of a professional radio announcer, slowly and distinctly. In a sense he sets the stage and creates the illusion of a real radio broadcast. The initials of the school might be used for station call letters.

The playing time indicated for each play is the average time a presentation will take, not counting any introductory or concluding music. This time may be varied by allotting more or less time to the pauses, sound effects, music, etc.

The author gratefully acknowledges the loan of scripts from Miss Clara Breed, Miss Toni Hult and the Young People's Department of the Milwaukee Public Library; and also invaluable help in preparing scripts from Mrs. Florette Nordlund, Mrs. Elizabeth Priddy, Mr. William Ratigan, Mrs. Manorma S. Stoecker and my Library Assistant in the Children's Department, Miss Carolyn Macartney.

KATHERINE WILLIAMS WATSON

Denver Public Library
August 1, 1947

Contents

Blue Willow

From the story, *Blue Willow*, by Doris Gates. Published by The Viking Press. Reproduced by permission of the publishers. Adapted for radio by Katherine Watson. (Grades 5-6)　　　20 minutes

Cast of Characters

JANEY LARKIN .... ten-year-old girl
LUPE ROMERO .... Mexican girl, same age
TONY ROMERO .... Lupe's brother
MOM .... Janey's stepmother
DAD .... Janey's father
MRS. ROMERO .... Lupe's mother
MANUEL ROMERO .... Lupe's father
LIBRARIAN
BOUNCE REYBURN .... rent collector
MR. ANDERSON .... landlord
MRS. ANDERSON .... his wife
DOCTOR
MISS PETERSON .... Janey's teacher

Sounds

Car starting　　　　　Bell ringing
Footsteps　　　　　　Door opening
Music　　　　　　　　Door closing

Blue Willow

ANNOUNCER: This is the story of ten-year-old Janey Larkin, whose father is an itinerant farm worker. Ever since dust and drought had driven them out of northern Texas, the Larkins—Janey, and her stepmother and Dad—had traveled hither and yon, wherever there were crops to be harvested. Janey's one cherished possession, inherited from happier days, when her real mother was alive, is a blue willow plate. Now they have reached the San Joaquin Valley in California; and Janey wants to stay here forever, because she finds friends her own age—Lupe, a little Mexican girl, and her brother Tony. The Larkins have been living in the board shack a week when we hear—

JANEY: What's the matter, Lupe?

LUPE: We're going to the fair and my mother says you can come too.

JANEY: What fair?

LUPE: The big fair in Fresno. There's one every year. Today is the first day and children get in free. Don't you want to go?

JANEY: Oh! do I want to! I'll have to ask Mom first. I've never been to a fair.

MOM: Are you dead sure it won't cost anything?

JANEY: That's what Lupe said.

LUPE: Honest, Mrs. Larkin, it's the truth. All of us kids are going and we sure couldn't if it wasn't free.

18

MOM: All right. You can start getting cleaned up while I go over and see Mrs. Romero. I want to be right sure I have the straight of all this. And I want to know for certain when you'll be coming back.

LUPE: Well, I'll be going home now. You can come over to our place as soon as you're ready. We won't leave without you.

JANEY: Thanks for remembering about me. It was kind.

LUPE: Oh, that's O.K. I wanted you.

MUSIC: *Up and out.*

MOM: Here's a clean handkerchief for you, Janey. You may need it. I tied a nickel in it. It's yours to spend any way you want to.

JANEY: I'll be careful not to lose it. Good-by, Mom.

SOUND: *Footsteps. Car starting.*

MRS. ROMERO: You are quiet, Janey. You shouldn't feel strange with us now. You must laugh and be glad because we have the whole afternoon to play.

JANEY: I am glad. You can't even begin to think how glad I am. If only we don't have to move and spoil everything.

MUSIC: *Bridge.*

MRS. ROMERO: Well, here we are at the fair.

LUPE: Over there's the Ferris wheel. It's always in the same place.

TONY: Let's look at the animals first.

JANEY: Why, I've never seen so many animals. They all look so clean.

LUPE: Now let's go to another building.

JANEY: Oh! look at all the different things. I've never seen such beautiful fruit.

MRS. ROMERO: Tired?

JANEY: No, just tempted. Let's get out of here before I start grabbing things.

LUPE: This next building has all kinds of exhibits. Oh! Look at the tricks of that magician!

JANEY: Let's go to that booth over there. Why, what is it? It looks like a real living-room.

LUPE: That's the liberry booth. Just books.

LIBRARIAN: Come in and rest a minute. These books are here for you to look at as long as you care to.

TONY: Come on. We're going to the merry-go-round.

JANEY: Mrs. Romero, I'd like to stay here a while. You all just go ahead anywhere you want to, and I'll stay here until you come back.

LUPE: Don't you want to ride on the merry-go-round?

JANEY: I'd rather stay here than go anywhere else.

MRS. ROMERO: Well, be sure then that you don't start off anywhere until we get back.

JANEY: I promise, Mrs. Romero, cross my heart and hope to die.

SOUND: *Footsteps receding.*

JANEY: Oh! I don't know where to start. These books all look so good. I think though I'd like to read this one.

MUSIC: *Bridge.*

SOUND: *Footsteps approaching.*

LUPE: I won the brass ring, Janey. It's good for a free ride, and I want you to have it.

JANEY: Thank you, Lupe, but I don't want it. It's your ride; and, besides, I have my own nickel. I don't need to be beholden to anyone.

LUPE: I've been riding so much, another would make me dizzy. That's why I thought I'd give the ride to you.

JANEY: Oh! I know you want to be kind, Lupe. All right. As long as you're sure you don't want it, I'll take it.

LUPE: No, I don't want it, Janey. It's O.K.

MUSIC: *Bridge.*

JANEY: Now, I've had the ride. I want to spend my five-cent piece. I know what I'll get. A package of gum. It's just the thing, too. Now we can all have some. Oh! What fun we've had today!

MUSIC: *Musical curtain.*

ANNOUNCER: Bounce Reyburn, a dishonest employee of Mr. Anderson, who owns the shack the Larkins call home, charges them rent without the owner's knowledge. Life is hard for them all. Fatigue weighs heavy and Mom, Janey's stepmother, falls ill. Janey goes for the doctor, taking her beloved willow plate to pay him.

DOCTOR: Well, who's sick?

JANEY: My mother, and she didn't want you to come and see her because we haven't much money left and the cotton is nearly all gone. But I have brought you the willow plate.

DOCTOR: How long has she been sick?

21

JANEY: She's had a cold three days.

DOCTOR: Good Lord! Pneumonia probably by now. Well, come along. Standing around here isn't doing her any good.

JANEY: But the plate! Don't you want it?

DOCTOR: No, I do not.

MUSIC: *Musical curtain.*

ANNOUNCER: Gradually Mom improved. Then came the day for Bounce to collect the rent.

BOUNCE: Well, I guess you know why I'm here, Mr. Larkin.

DAD: Yes, I do.

BOUNCE: Well, let's have it.

DAD: Sorry, Reyburn, but I can't pay you anything this month. We would have been out of here this week if my wife hadn't got sick. She can't start traveling again for some time. Cotton picking is over and I don't know whether I'll be able to find any more work. I've got to keep what little I have left for food. As far as this shack is concerned, it isn't worth the rent you're asking; and if we moved out, nobody'd live in it again this winter, and you know it.

BOUNCE: Listen, buddy, there's no use whinin' about your hard luck to me. It's either pay or get out. Savvy?

DAD: Well, get this and get it straight. I'm not paying up and I'm not moving out. And what would you like to do about it?

MOM: Pay him and get rid of him. Fighting will only get us all into trouble. He could have you arrested, Jim, and then where would we be? You haven't got a chance.

22

DAD: I won't pay him. Right's right and wrong's wrong.

JANEY: Wait! Wait! I've thought of something. Here's the willow plate in the suitcase. We'll pay the rent with this.

MOM: Oh, no, Janey.

BOUNCE: What do I want with somebody's old plate?

JANEY: It's so pretty. It must be worth five dollars. Besides, it's the only thing we have left.

BOUNCE: You set quite a store by this, don't you? O.K. It's a deal.

SOUND: *Footsteps receding.*

MOM: That was a brave thing you did, Janey.

JANEY: It was just an old plate.

MOM: I know what it meant to you. I've known all the time. It was your mother's. You shouldn't have had to give it up.

MUSIC: *Musical curtain.*

ANNOUNCER: Mom continued to improve. Dad tried to find work, and Janey kept busy—so busy that at times she almost forgot about the willow plate. Almost, but never entirely. There was some comfort in knowing that at last it had found a decent home. For, of course, Janey believed that Bounce had turned it over to Mr. Anderson, the owner. We now hear Miss Peterson, Janey's former school teacher from the camp school, who has brought them some fruit.

MISS PETERSON: As soon as you are able to spare her, I want Janey to come to school.

DAD: There's no use her starting to school now. As soon as my wife is able to travel, and maybe before that, we'll be leaving. There's no more work around here, and we've got to be heading toward the Imperial Valley if we don't want to lose out all around.

MISS PETERSON: Of course, I understand, but I'll be hoping to see you again soon, Janey.

MUSIC: *Musical curtain.*

ANNOUNCER: And she did. It was on Christmas Day, and again her arms were full of bundles. Janey hadn't thought much about its being Christmas. The money in the buckskin bag was running low, and they must move on while there was still enough left to buy gasoline and the things they would need before Dad found work again. So it wasn't a very merry Christmas. It is now a few days later and we hear Dad saying—

DAD: We'll be on our way tomorrow.

JANEY: [*To herself*] Oh! I just can't go away without telling the willow plate good-by. I'm sure Mom and Dad won't mind my going.

MUSIC: *Bridge.*

JANEY: My, but it's cold. Well, I'm almost there. Oh! here's the house. I'll just ring the bell.

SOUND: *Bell ringing. Door opening.*

JANEY: I want to speak to Mr. Anderson, please.

MRS. ANDERSON: Won't you come in?

SOUND: *Door closing.*

MRS. ANDERSON: Someone to see you, Nils.

24

MR. ANDERSON: Hello! Won't you sit down and tell me what I can do for you?

JANEY: I'm Janey Larkin.

MR. ANDERSON: This is Mrs. Anderson, Janey.

JANEY: Pleased to meet you. I've come to tell the willow plate good-by. We're going tomorrow and I couldn't bear to go without seeing it once more.

MR. ANDERSON: The willow plate? What willow plate?

JANEY: Don't you remember? Bounce took it a while ago for the rent.

MR. ANDERSON: Bounce! What's Bounce got to do with all this?

JANEY: Why, Bounce is the one who collects your rent for you! We didn't have the money last time, so we gave him the willow plate instead.

MR. ANDERSON: Suppose you tell me the whole story from the very beginning. I want all of it.

JANEY: Well, you see—[*Fading out*]

MUSIC: *Bridge.*

MR. ANDERSON: Why didn't you come to me before?

JANEY: There wasn't any reason to come. I wouldn't be here now if I hadn't wanted to see the willow plate once more.

MR. ANDERSON: Well, you see, Janey, I didn't know anything about the rent. Whatever money Bounce got from you, he kept. I have never seen the willow plate. But I intend to see it very soon.

JANEY: But where is it?

25

MR. ANDERSON: I think the plate will have to wait a little while. I want to talk to your father before I talk to Bounce. It wouldn't surprise me a bit, Janey, if you didn't leave here tomorrow.

JANEY: Honest? Oh! I wish we could stay.

MR. ANDERSON: You're a funny little coot.

MRS. ANDERSON: I'm going with you to the Larkins, Nils.

MR. ANDERSON: Good. I'll get the car.

SOUND: *Car starting.*

ANNOUNCER: With Nils Anderson's visit to the shack, the lives and fortunes of the Larkins were changed. Never again would they be wanderers upon the earth; never again would Janey long in vain to go to a "regular" school. Mr. Anderson was shown the receipts which Bounce had signed and which were proof of his dishonesty. And now we hear these two men talking together.

DAD: I guess we shouldn't have just stayed in this shack without saying anything to anybody. You forget about such fine points when you live as we do.

MR. ANDERSON: Of course you should have. You're not the first family to occupy this shack. It has no value except to people like you, and anyone has been welcome to use it. As far as that goes, I knew somebody was in it this fall, because I had seen you around here when I came over this way; and I had no objections to your staying. Of course, I'd no idea of what Bounce was up to. He's probably been grafting on everyone who's moved in here.

DAD: Well, that's about all the story.

26

Mr. Anderson: I'm letting Bounce go tomorrow, Larkin. I'll need a man in his place. The job is yours if you want it. Seventy-five dollars a month, a house, and all the eggs and milk you can use.

Dad: Oh! Thank you, sir.

Mr. Anderson: Take it easy there, Larkin. You deserve a break and I'm glad I can give it to you. I'll expect you to move in tomorrow. Good night.

Sound: *Footsteps receding.*

Mom: What he said was the truth. You do deserve a break. I'm glad it's come.

Dad: I guess we have Janey to thank for it.

Mom: We should give thanks to that Power which is greater than Janey, greater than all of us.

Janey: [*To herself*] I'm not sure whether Mom means God or the willow plate—so I'll say a silent prayer to both.

Music: *Musical curtain.*

Announcer: Loading the car next day was sheer fun. It was the first time Jancy could remember when it ever had been fun. How different this moving was from all the others! We now hear Janey talking to Lupe, who had run across the road before the arrival of the school bus.

Lupe: Now, Janey you can go to my school. You will be in my class because we are the same age; and Miss Peterson, who was your teacher at the camp school will be your teacher again.

Janey: Yes, and we can ride together on the bus. I'll get picked up first because I will be farther from town than you.

27

LUPE: No. We won't ride together in the bus.

JANEY: But why not? You're not planning to miss it every day, are you?

LUPE: We are moving into town. My mother is going to start an eating place and make enchiladas. We will live back of the place.

JANEY: How nice! But why didn't you tell me this before?

LUPE: I don't know. You were so sad.

JANEY: You know, Lupe—I'm glad you are my friend. We'll be seeing each other now at school; and you can visit me week ends, and I can visit you. Perhaps we can both help with the enchiladas. Oh, I'm so glad we're not going away.

LUPE: Good-by—until tomorrow, then.

SOUND: *Car starting.*

MUSIC: *Bridge.*

JANEY: Oh! here's our house, and my willow plate on the table. I'm never going to let you go again. Never!

DAD: And look—three five-dollar bills.

JANEY: Where did they come from?

DAD: They're what Bounce collected from us for rent. Mr. Anderson held them out of his wages when he settled up with him.

MOM: Now we can pay Dr. Pierce. I guess he can use the money to good purpose. And we won't be beholden to him any longer.

DAD: Now you just sit still, Mom, for you are not very strong. Janey and I will clean up the place.

28

JANEY: Now can we put the willow plate out where we can always see it, instead of in the suitcase?

MOM: This isn't a proper home. It's only a tank-house, even if it is comfortable. That plate came out of a real house and it's never going to be set out in anything but a real home.

ANNOUNCER: The Larkins soon settled into their new way of life, and no family in the San Joaquin Valley was happier. Janey went to the district school; and instead of a skinny little girl, she now looked well and healthy. Mom was different too. The tired look had gone from her face, and she smiled more readily these days. Dad was the same happy-go-lucky Dad, but his voice had a confident ring that Janey hadn't heard since she was a tiny girl in Texas. And now it is spring, and Lupe announced to Janey one day—

LUPE: I know a secret and it's about something you wished for once.

JANEY: What is it?

LUPE: I can't tell because it's a secret, but you'll like it when you know.

JANEY: When will I know?

LUPE: Pretty soon.

JANEY: But there isn't anything I want now, Lupe. If you could hand me the whole world, there wouldn't be a thing in it I want, that I haven't already.

LUPE: You wait and see.

ANNOUNCER: So in a way, Janey was a little prepared when one Saturday Lupe's father, Manuel, and six other Mexicans drove into the yard of the Anderson ranch. Janey had a feeling the instant she saw them that they had something to do with the secret. **Mr.**

29

Anderson appeared while the other men lifted wooden forms out of the truck. Janey walks over to Manuel and says—

JANEY: What are you going to do, Mr. Romero?

MANUEL: We're starting to build a house, an adobe house. It will be cool in summer, warm in winter; and it will last for anyway two hundred years. Will that be long enough, do you think?

JANEY: Who's going to live in the new house, Mr. Anderson?

MR. ANDERSON: Why, I kind of hoped you would, Janey. Here's the plan. How do you think you'll like it?

JANEY: Oh, it's to have four rooms and a bath, and a fireplace. That's where we can put the willow plate. I've never been so happy in all my life. How long can we stay, Mr. Anderson?

MR. ANDERSON: As long as you want to, Janey.

JANEY: Lupe, ask me how long we can stay.

LUPE: Mr. Anderson just told you.

JANEY: That doesn't make any difference. Ask me. I want you to.

LUPE: How long are you going to stay, Janey?

JANEY: [*Happily*] As long as we want to.

Down, Down the Mountain

From *Down, Down the Mountain,* by Ellis Credle. Published by
Thomas Nelson & Sons. Reproduced by permission of the author.
Adapted for radio by Elizabeth Priddy and Katherine Watson.
(Grades 3-4)   15 minutes

CAST OF CHARACTERS

HETTY⎫
  ⎬ .... sister and brother
HANK ⎭

MAMMY⎫
  ⎬ .... their parents
PAPPY ⎭

GRANNY .... their grandmother
OLD MAN
OLD LADY
KIND LADY
2ND MAN
3RD MAN

SOUNDS

Footsteps   Rumble of wagons
Horses' hoofs   Running feet
Running water   Auctioneer's voice
Gobble of turkeys   Whistle of train
Bell ringing   Music
Thump of sack   Voices of crowd

31

Down, Down the Mountain

ANNOUNCER: This is a story of Hank and Hetty, who lived in the Blue Ridge Mountains. They raised some fine turnips to trade for some shiny, creaky shoes. Listen how their kindness of heart almost defeated their plan!

HETTY: [*Excitedly*] New shoes! Soon now, Hank, we're going to have new creaky, squeaky shoes!

HANK: Careful! Careful, Hetty! You're spilling the water!

HETTY: But I'm so very happy—and there is more water—

HANK: [*Wearily*] Yes, more water way down beyond the cabin. I'm tired of carrying water way up hill from the stream!

HETTY: But it won't be much longer now, Hank. Just see how big our turnips have grown! Oh, wasn't it grand of Granny to think up this way for us to earn our shoes?

HANK: Funny Pappy and Mammy didn't think of it when we asked them. All Pappy did was to shake his head and say, "Shoes? Why, there's no money in our house for shoes!"

HETTY: And Mammy just said the only place we could get shiny shoes was in town, way down the mountain!

HANK: But pretty soon we'll be going down the mountain to the town!

HETTY: [*Excitedly*] And to get some new shoes—oh, Hank!

HANK: We'd better wait until we sell the turnips before we plan too much.

HETTY: [*Happily*] Here come Mammy and Pappy and Granny now. I told them to come up to see our turnips.

SOUND: *Footsteps.*

HANK: Mammy—Pappy—Granny—see! Here is our turnip patch we have worked on all summer. Now we can have our shiny, creaky, squeaky shoes!

GRANNY: You must have worked very hard! Yes, indeedy! Yes, indeedy!

PAPPY: Um! So these are your turnips! Mighty fine showin' too. Don't know as I ever did see a finer batch!

MAMMY: [*Surprised*] Why, just look at the size of them turnips! My! My!

HETTY: We carried water all summer for them when they were dry—

HANK: And hoed them and—chased away bugs and worms.

PAPPY: Yes—yes—and now let me think—tomorrow? Um— yes, I do believe I can let you two have the old gray horse to take them into town tomorrow!

MAMMY: Then we had better all get to work and get them pulled and washed off and in the sack so you can get an early start!

PAPPY: It's getting a bit late and the shadows are creepin' over the mountain, so you young-ones better tramp down to the cabin with Mammy and get to bed. I'll get these turnips ready for market tomorrow!

HETTY: All right, Pappy! We'll hurry right to bed!

HANK: Come on then, Hetty, I'll race you down to the cabin.

MUSIC: *Musical curtain.*

MAMMY: Now don't forget! Just follow the trail down the mountain and soon you'll come to the town.

HANK: Don't you worry, Mammy; I'll take care of us!

GRANNY: It's a long, long trip for two young-ones!

HETTY: But we'll be careful, Granny.

PAPPY: Well, here's your horse. Now climb up, the two of you, and I'll swing this sack of turnips in front of you—that's right—there now, up—up—now you're ready!

MAMMY: And you'd better be on your way—time's flyin' by and you've a long day's trip—

GRANNY: That's right—that's right—better get along now. Get up, get up, old boy, and good-by, children.

ALL: Good-by! Good-by! Good-by!

SOUND: *Horse hoofs up and fade.*

MUSIC: *Bridge.*

HETTY: Hank! Hank—what's that man doing? Over there in the field—

HANK: Just cuttin' his cane. Probably gettin' it ready for market.

OLD MAN: Howdy there—where you two goin' so early?

HANK: We're takin' our turnips into town to sell them.

HETTY: And we are going to buy some new shiny shoes with the money!

OLD MAN: Well, now that'll be fine. What did you say they were, turnips? A nice juicy turnip would taste pretty good for dinner tonight—

34

HETTY: We can spare a few for him, can't we, Hank?

HANK: Sure—we've plenty. Here sir, hope you'll enjoy them.

OLD MAN: Thanky—thanky—to you two—and a good trip —Good-by.

HANK and HETTY: Good-by, sir, good-by!

MUSIC: *Bridge.*

HANK: Hetty, look over there. See the old woman making soap in her iron kettle. Doesn't she remind you of Granny?

OLD LADY: Good mornin', children—you're up early.

HETTY: Good mornin', ma'am. Yes, we're on our way to town to sell our turnips!

OLD LADY: Turnips! Um! Been a long time since I had a turnip. My old man does like 'em, too!

HETTY: We can spare them a couple, can't we, Hank?

OLD LADY: My, such big ones. Um, thank you now, and they'll make us a fine supper.

HANK: Well, we must travel on now. We hope you do enjoy the turnips. Good-by.

OLD LADY: [*Voice fading*] Good-by to you both.

SOUND: *Hoof beats.*

HETTY: My, this slope is steep, Hank. Watch out. I'm about to slide off.

HANK: You'll have to watch out for yourself, I guess. I've a big enough job keepin' this sack from sliding off. What—whoa, boy—

HETTY: Oh! Hank, look! The trail ends down there at the stream. Oh—

SOUND: *Running water in stream.*

HANK: That's funny; that sure is funny. Mammy said just to follow the trail, and now it's gone. What do you suppose we'd better do?

KIND LADY: Well now, what are you doin' way down here at the stream?

HANK: We've—we've lost the trail goin' down the mountain to town—

KIND LADY: Ha, ha, so that's what's worrying you. Why, there isn't any trail from here down—you just have to travel down the stream.

HETTY: Oh, thank you. Thank you, ma'am. We thought we were lost. Wouldn't you like a few turnips? We do want you to know how much you have helped us.

KIND LADY: Now, that's right kind of you. My! Those are sure fine turnips. Well, have a nice trip.

HANK and HETTY: Good-by. Good-by.

MUSIC: *Bridge.*

SOUND: *Turkeys and footsteps.*

2ND MAN: Well! Well! What a big bag you have on your horse! What's in it?

HANK: They're turnips that we're going to sell in town.

HETTY: And then we're going to buy some creaky, squeaky shoes.

2ND MAN: Turnips! Oh, how hungry that makes me. Why! I've had nary a bite to eat since breakfast at daybreak. And driving a flock of turkeys sure gives one a hunger.

HANK: We could spare a few if that would help—here.

2ND MAN: Now, you're the kind young-ones. Thanky.

HANK: Well, we just must be getting on now. It can't be very much further to town.

HETTY: It isn't. It isn't. Oh, Hank, look ahead. *There's* the town.

SOUND: *Bell ringing.*

HANK· See, Hetty, that building there is the school—hear the bell.

SOUND: *Voices of crowd fade in.*

HETTY: And there's the church and the courthouse and—and—

HANK: And here's the store. Whoa! Whoa, old boy.

HETTY: Oh, Hank—at last.

HANK: Well, come on, Hetty. Jump down; this is where we trade our turnips for new shoes. I'll get the sack of turnips down.

HETTY: Hank—Hank—the sack looks—it looks so thin.

SOUND: *Thumps sack.*

HANK: It—it is awful empty like—but wait, I'll reach in—Oh! Hetty—Oh! Hetty, look—

HETTY: One turnip—one turnip—is—is that *all* there is left, Hank?

HANK: It's the biggest one we had—but—but I don't think it'll be enough.

HETTY: They're there, in the window, Hank—see—the shiny, creaky, squeaky shoes. Oh, dear!

HANK: There, now, no use to cry any—that won't help— Come, let's walk about a bit while we think—

HETTY: Might just as well before we start home—

SOUND: *Whistle and toot of train.*

HETTY: Oh, Hank—it's a train—look over there.

HANK: Say! But look there at those covered wagons, all loaded down with apples. Um-mmm, don't they look good? Let's go over there by the courthouse—see, they're selling horses.

SOUND: *Rumble of wagons. Auctioneer's voice.*

HETTY: But, Hank, what do you suppose all those people are doing over there? It says "County Fair" on the sign—

HANK: We can go over to see. Here, I'll carry the turnip a bit.

3RD MAN: Pumpkins on this table, please—vegetables over yonder—tomatoes on the first table—

HANK: Whee! Just look at the turnips, Hetty.

HETTY: But none of them are as fine as ours.

3RD MAN: Howdy. Want to enter your turnip, you two?

HANK: Enter?

3RD MAN: Yes, enter it in the contest. Best turnip gets the prize.

HETTY: Let's, Hank! Let's enter it!

HANK: Sure. Our names—are Hetty and Hank.

3RD MAN: Good thing you got here when you did, 'cause we're just ready for the judging—now let's see—this one is a very juicy one, but not so big—and this one is big but not so juicy—but this one—say now, this one is both juicy and big. This—this turnip, ladies and gentlemen, is the winner. Hetty—Hank—here is a five dollar gold piece for your prize.

HETTY: Oh—oh, thank you so much. Hank come, now we *can* get our shiny shoes—hurry—let's run.

SOUND: *Running feet.*

The Lance of Kanana

From *The Lance of Kanana*, by Henry Willard French. Published by Lothrop, Lee & Shepard Company. Reproduced by permission of the publishers. Adapted for radio by Clara E. Breed. (Grades 5-6)   15 minutes

Cast of Characters

FATHER .. Kanana's father, called the Terror of the Desert

KANANA .... Bedouin boy of thirteen years

OLD WOMAN .... occupant of perch next to Kanana

WOUNDED SOLDIER .... Arab soldier

CALIPH OMAR .... Arabian ruler

MANUEL .... Greek general

1ST SOLDIER

2ND SOLDIER

KAHLED .... Arabian general

Sounds

Horses' hoofs on sand
Feet running on sand
Famished man gulping
      water
Breaking of seal

Opening of letter
Tearing of cloth
Cheers
Shouts
Noise and confusion

The Lance of Kanana

ANNOUNCER: Come with us as our players take us to the faraway land of Arabia, to learn of the excitement and heroism of those early times on the burning desert sands—particularly the story of "The Lance of Kanana."

Kanana [*ka-na-na*] was an Arab—a Bedouin [*be-doo-in*] boy of many years ago, born upon the desert, of the seed of Ishmael, [*ish-may-el*] of the tribe of Beni Sad [*bay-nee-sad*]. It seems strange that a Bedouin boy could have lived who was not accustomed to the use of the sword and lance long before he reached the dignity of manhood. Kanana had never held a lance in his hand but once. Yet many a celebrated sheik and powerful chieftain of his day lies dead, buried, and forgotten, while the name of Kanana is still a magic battle cry among the sons of Ishmael. His lance is one of the most precious relics of Arabia.

As a young boy, Kanana had been the shepherd of his father's sheep; but now that he was thirteen years old, it was time that he should take his place among the fighting men of his tribe—listen, while his father talks to him—

FATHER: [*Impatiently*] For the third time, art thou ready to be a man?—

KANANA: [*Firmly*] My father, I cannot lift a lance to take a life, unless it be for Allah and Arabia.

FATHER: Knowest thou not the old decree that the hand of the Ishmaelite [*ish-may-el-ite*] must be against every man, and every man's hand against him?

41

KANANA: I know, my father. But the war of the desert is murder and robbery. [*Pleading*] I am taught that Allah created the animals and cares for them, and that I cannot please him if I allow them to suffer. It must be, surely, that men are more precious to Allah than animals. Why must we kill one another, even if we are Arabs and Ishmaelites?

FATHER: [*Angry*] Thou art a coward, and darest not fight! Go then, coward, with the women and children, and frighten the birds from the ripening grain! Go to the farthest perch, so that I need not see thee and be reminded that my son is a coward!

ANNOUNCER: There was not one of the tribe but felt Kanana richly deserved this disgrace. For three weeks Kanana stayed upon his perch, doing a woman's work— frightening birds away from the grain with his sling shot. No other Bedouin could throw a stone from his sling so far and so accurately. But his heart was not in his work and on a hot morning we find him sitting crosslegged on his perch, trying to think out some way to convince his father that he is not a coward.

OLD WOMAN: [*Calling from a distance*] Hi, there! you lazy son of a brave father! Look at the birds about you! Are you dead or only sleeping?

KANANA: [*Rousing himself*] Only thinking—thoughts that get me nowhere!

SOUND: *Horses' hoofs on sandy soil. Approach Kanana— then stop.*

FATHER: [*Angrily*] Oh Kanana, Kanana! Thou son of my old age, why didst thou come into the world to shame me? When thou shakest the cream, the butter is spoiled. When thou tendest the sheep, they are lost. When thou watchest the grain, it is eaten before thy

42

face. What shall a father do with a son who will not lift his hand among men? And now when all the miseries of life have taken hold upon me, thou sittest at thine ease to mock me!

KANANA: My father, slay me and I will take it as a mercy from thy hand! Or, as I am fit for nothing here, bid me go, and among strangers will I beg. But do not, my father, speak of me as ungrateful. [*Puzzled*] I know of no flood of sorrow that has come down upon thee.

FATHER: [*Fiercely*] Knowest thou not what they all know?

KANANA: I know of nothing, my father. Since I came into the field three weeks ago, no one has spoken to me but to scold me.

FATHER: Then know now that one of thy brave brothers has been taken prisoner by Raschid Airikat. [*rash-id*] The other has returned, wounded and helpless. The whole caravan with the white camel at its head, Raschid has taken; and he has turned with it toward Damascus. Oh! that I had a son remaining, who could lift a lance against this Raschid in revenge!

KANANA: [*Earnestly*] My father, give me a horse, a sack of grain, a skin of water, and I will follow after Raschid Airikat. I will not slay him, but, by the help of Allah, I will bring to thee thy white camel with my brother seated upon his back.

FATHER: [*Scornful*] Thou wisp of flax before a fire! Thou seed before a wind! Get thee back to thy perch and thy birds. See if thou canst keep awake until sundown. Harvesting begins with the daylight.

KANANA: [*Calmly*] My father, I will watch the birds till sundown. Then let others do the reaping. Kanana, whom thou scornest, will be far away upon the desert, to seek and find his brother.

43

FATHER: [*Astonished*] Did I not say I would not trust a horse to thee?

KANANA: These feet of mine can do my bidding well enough. And by the beard of the Prophet, they shall do it, till they have returned to thee thy son and thy white camel. I would do something, oh, my father, that I too might have thy blessing and not thy curse. Now say to me if I bring them back, then thou wilt bless me too, aye, even though still I will not lift a lance, unless it be for Allah and Arabia.

FATHER: [*With scornful pity*] Yes, then I will bless thee.

ANNOUNCER: The moment the sun went down, Kanana left his perch. With a sack of grain slung over his shoulder, he started walking across the desert. Two nights he walked, resting in the daytime from the furious heat of the sun. At sunrise the second morning, he stopped near an oasis to examine some marks on the ground—

KANANA: [*Talking to himself*] A caravan has camped here—spears of grass left—that camel has lost a front tooth—ah, this mark! That camel was lame in the left knee—ants! The caravan was carrying honey. [*With satisfaction*] My brother and the white camel are not ten hours from here on the road to Mecca!—But what is that sound?

WOUNDED SOLDIER: [*Very weak*] Water! Water! In the name of Allah give me water.

SOUND: *Feet running on sand.*

KANANA: What has happened? Thou art wounded! Here is water. Let me hold the cup to thy lips!

SOUND: *Famished man gulping water.*

44

WOUNDED SOLDIER: More! Give me more!

SOUND: *Drinking of water.*

WOUNDED SOLDIER: [*Speaking with difficulty*] You are a beardless youth, but you are an Arab—listen to me— the mighty Prince Constantine, [*kon-stan-tine*], son of the Greek Emperor, is coming to sweep the Arab from the face of the earth. We are bearing a letter to the Caliph Omar, [*ka-lif o-mar*] who is now in Mecca, telling him of the danger and asking help. If the letter does not reach him, Arabia is lost. Robbers have killed my companions and stolen our horses, and I am dying. In the name of Allah, will you fly with this to the great Caliph?

KANANA: In the name of Allah, I will.

ANNOUNCER: Three weeks later, weary and travel-worn, Kanana reached Mecca. As he entered the city gates he passed a caravan—led by his father's white camel! He laid his hand upon the camel's nose in greeting as he passed, but he did not stop—a few moments later we find him at the palace, bowing before the throne of the Caliph.

KANANA: A message for the Caliph Omar.

SOUND: *Seal being broken—letter opened.*

CALIPH: And who art thou?

KANANA: I am Kanana, son of the Terror of the Desert.

CALIPH: A beardless youth! And dost thou know aught of the import of this letter?

KANANA: Oh, sir, the Arab soldier who gave it to me said that if the message did not reach the great Caliph, Arabia would be lost.

CALIPH: 'Tis even so. But how came living man to trust a boy like thee to come alone through the streets of Mecca with such a message?

KANANA: I came alone with the letter from the oasis at Mount Hor. The soldier was dying and begged me to bring it. Three weeks I have guarded this letter through dangers.

CALIPH: Thou art a brave youth! Would to Allah that every Arab had thy heart! Thou hast done what many a brave man would not have dared attempt. Ask what reward thou wilt of me!

KANANA: I would have thy blessing, Caliph Omar.

CALIPH: Thou shalt have it, my son. And camels or sheep or gold. Ask what thou wilt!

KANANA: Give me thy blessing and let me go!

CALIPH: If I can do nothing for thee, there is yet something which thou canst do for me. Kahled [*ka-led*] is the greatest general who fights for the Prophet. My orders must reach him, and quickly. A company of soldiers will start tonight for his camp at Bashra [*bas-ra*]. It would be well for thee to go with them, to give the story to Kahled by word of mouth.

KANANA: The way is hard. The sand is deep and dry.

CALIPH: [*Surprised*] Hardship should not be hard for thee!

KANANA: The way is dangerous.

CALIPH: [*Astonished*] Thou! son of the Terror of the Desert, speaking of danger!

KANANA: Oh, mighty Omar, I spoke for thy soldiers. Before they reach the sands of Bashra, they will be with the five who started with this letter. Give me the

46

letters, and with thy blessing and the help of Allah, I will deliver them! He who guarded me will guard me still.

CALIPH: By the beard of the Prophet, there is both foolishness and wisdom in thy words. Thou shalt take the messages by one route, and by another I will send the soldiers with copies. When wilt thou start?

KANANA: Now!

CALIPH: Well spoken! What camels and servants shall be provided?

KANANA: Oh mighty Omar, as I came through the city gates, I noted a white camel. I would have it and its driver, and the swiftest dromedary in Mecca, with grain for fourteen days.

CALIPH: They shall be ready for thee in half an hour. When thy mission is finished, they shall be thy reward. My son, this is not thy last mission. I read it in thy destiny that thou wilt succeed and succeed again, until the name of Kanana be written among the greatest of those who have lifted the lance for Allah and Arabia. Go now, and may Allah go with thee!

ANNOUNCER: After the message was delivered to Kahled's camp, Kanana, true to his promise, sent the white camel home to his father, with his brother seated upon its back. Kahled sent Kanana on other dangerous missions, which he performed with courage and daring and great cleverness. There came a time, however, when Kanana was taken prisoner by the opposing army [*Fading slowly*] and was brought before the Greek general, Prince Manuel.

MANUEL: [*Fading in—stern*] 'Twas you who told Kahled where we would be camped.

KANANA: It was I.

47

MANUEL: Do you not fear to die?

KANANA: Nay, I fear nothing.

MANUEL: I am about to torture you. Have you anything to say before the work begins?

KANANA: Among the captives taken by the prince, I saw an old man. May it please the prince to double every torture he has prepared for me and to set that old man free?

MANUEL: Who is he? [*Pause*] He shall die unless you tell me.

KANANA: [*Whispering*] He is my father.

MANUEL: You have offered to suffer torture if I will set your father free. But that does not pay your debt to me. You gave to Kahled the information by which he conquered Jababal [*jab-bab-bal*]. But for you, I should be on my way to Mecca to sweep it from the earth. But I like courage, and you have shown it. It is a pity to throw a heart like yours under a clod of earth, and I will give you an opportunity to save both yourself and your father.

KANANA: What is it?

MANUEL: Stand upon the brow of that cliff yonder. As the sun comes up, wave this lance about your head and shout your own name and your father's so that all your people in the valley below can hear. Tell them that in one hour, thirty thousand Arabs will desert their own leader and draw the sword in Manuel's army! Then throw the lance, and if your aim be good and you kill an Arab, I will set your father free! Refuse and I will not only torture and slay you, but your father also.

KANANA: Will the prince allow his captive to sit alone till sunrise and consider his offer?

MANUEL: [*Calling to a soldier*] Take him out upon the cliff and let him sit alone! [*Grimly*] And have the irons heated for the torture!

ANNOUNCER: Kanana chose a spot where he could overlook the valley and whatever his intentions may have been, he changed them instantly with his first glance. In the gray distance he saw that laden camels were moving to the south. Kahled the Invincible had ordered a retreat! Kanana knew that to retreat at that moment meant death to Arabia, and he made his decision. Soon an officer touched him on the shoulder. In a moment more the sun would rise. Kanana rose and walked to the cliff's edge.

KANANA: Is the word of the prince unchanged? If I speak the words and throw the lance and kill an Arab, that moment thou wilt set my father free?

MANUEL: I swear it.

KANANA: Give me the lance! [*Pause*] No, give me a heavier one! The handrest on this one is too small for a Bedouin. But wait! I can remedy that myself with a bit of cloth.

SOUND: *Tearing cloth.*

KANANA: Now it fits my hand. That is better. [*Pause*]

MANUEL: What are you waiting for? Are you afraid? Remember your father.

KANANA: Seest yonder a man on a gray horse, moving slowly among the soldiers? He is coming nearer, nearer. That man is Kahled the Invincible. If he should come within range of the lance of Kanana, I suppose then Manuel would be well pleased to wait?

MANUEL: [*Pleased*] Good boy! Brave boy! When you have made up your mind to do a thing, you do it

49

admirably. Kill him, and you shall be loaded down with gold until the day you die of old age.

KANANA: [*Tense*] He has left the line of soldiers and rides along nearer the cliff! Now is my chance. [*In a loud voice*] I am Kanana, son of the Terror of the Desert! In one hour thirty thousand Arabs will draw the sword in the army of Manuel!

MANUEL: Now—with all thy strength—the lance. Good aim. [*Disappointed*] No. You but killed his horse.

VOICES FROM VALLEY BELOW: Kanana, the traitor! A curse upon Kanana! Traitor!

MANUEL: You did well, but you did not kill an Arab. It was for that I made my promise.

KANANA: [*Gasping*] "And if you kill an Arab, that moment I will set your father free." Those were the prince's words! That was his promise, bound by all the powers of earth and heaven! He will keep it. For I have killed an Arab! [*Fast fading*].

VOICES: He's jumped! He's killed himself—[*Noise and confusion*]

MANUEL: [*Dazed*] He has killed himself! A monstrous sacrifice! Set his father free, and tell him a great price has just been paid to buy his liberty!

ANNOUNCER: But the full importance of what had happened, Manuel did not know. Kahled's army did not retreat, as he had expected. A great battle was fought, in which Manuel's army was completely wiped out. Afterward, the Arabian soldiers gathered around Kahled's tent to do him honor.

SOUND: *Cheers—victorious shouting.*

1ST SOLDIER: Kahled! Kahled the Invincible!

50

2ND SOLDIER: Kahled the Great! Kahled the Invincible!

1ST SOLDIER: He is coming out. The tent flap moves. [*Cheers*]

SOUND: *Greater cheers—quickly fading away.*

2ND SOLDIER: He carries a heavy burden in his arms, wrapped in a sheepskin cloak.

KAHLED: [*Very solemn*] Behold! The body of Kanana! Thou sawest him throw this lance at me. Thou didst call him traitor. But about the handrest there was wound this strip of cloth. See! In blood—in his blood these words are written here: "Do not retreat! The infidels are starving and dying. Strike them in the rear!" It was his only means of reaching me. It was not the act of a traitor. No! It was the lance of Kanana that rescued Arabia!

River Children

From *River Children,* by Mary Brewster Hollister. Published by Dodd, Mead & Company. Reproduced by permission of the author. Adapted for radio by Florette Luce Nordlund. (Grades 5-6)

30 minutes

CAST OF CHARACTERS

BING-HU .... Chinese boy

ME-HWA .... his sister

DEA-DEA .... their baby brother

LIANG-AU .... boat-woman

U-SEE .... dog

UNCLE

AUNT

SOUNDS

Oriental music	Door opening and closing
Oars in water	Duck quacking
Scratching of match	Falling boxes, chests, etc.
Dog whimpering and barking	Splash of child falling into sea

River Children

ANNOUNCER: Would you like to live in a little amber-colored sampan and ferry passengers across the River Min in China? You would like to? Then you will enjoy hearing how courageous Bing-hu and his sister, Me-hwa, rescued their baby brother, Dea-dea, from the Evil Uncle. Bing-hu, Me-hwa, and Dea-dea are River Children and live alone on a boat on the River Min in Foochow, China.

All day long Bing-hu and Me-hwa row their little sampan up and down and across the River Min, looking for passengers to ferry across; for these children must buy their own rice to feed themselves and Baby Dea-dea.

When their lovely, gay mother and their understanding father were living, life was different. Bing-hu and Me-hwa had planned to be scholars and study in the Great Learning Hall on the hill where the Good-to-Love Lady taught. The Good-to-Love Lady had been a boat girl. She, too, was the daughter of River People. From the Great Learning Hall on the hill, she kept tender watch over these orphaned children.

MUSIC: *Fade in soft strains of oriental music. Keep under.*

ANNOUNCER: Right now, Bing-hu and Me-hwa are sitting on the pier, watching the twinkling lights of the Lantern Procession. The Lantern Festival is a very important event in China. Baby Dea-dea is asleep in the sampan-home while a good friend, Liang-au, a neighboring boat-woman, watches near him. [*Voice fading*]

ME-HWA: [*Fading in*] So many lanterns and banners I have never seen before! Look! Who is that red and green monster in the gold chair?

BING-HU: That's the old Demon-Chaser himself.

ME-HWA: [*Frightened*] Bing-hu, will the demons come this way when they are chased?

BING-HU: [*Laughing*] Of course not, sister! Not with all these lanterns about us. Lanterns scare the demons away.

ME-HWA: [*Unconvinced*] But it's dark on our little boat where Dea-dea sleeps. Dea-dea, Little Gold and Precious Jewels! Anyway, I'll be glad when the last lantern has passed. I do not like to leave Dea-dea so long.

BING-HU: Liang-au is with Dea-dea.

ME-HWA: Wasn't Dea-dea cunning, fast asleep with his head on U-see's woolly mop?

BING-HU: Ai—he was cunning. U-see will bark if anyone comes near.

ME-HWA: Bing-hu, it is nearly a year now since the Festival of the Dragon Boat Race.

BING-HU: Ai! I was thinking that too. All that day we had passengers! We rowed all day with our Good-to-Love Lady and her betrothed, the Honorable First Born!

ME-HWA: Um! I can still taste the cakes that Honorable First Born took from his red and gold lacquer basket.

BING-HU: I do like rice cakes!

ME-HWA: We were so happy—until we saw Uncle.

BING-HU: Ach! That Evil One! He kept following us in his red and yellow sampan. I tried so hard to keep out of his way!

ME-HWA: He waited until our passengers had left. Then he bottled us up in that narrow place by the Customs Jetty.

BING-HU: And made me hand him all our earnings!

ME-HWA: Not all, Bing-hu! Have you forgotten the two dollars our passengers had given us—the two dollars I had hidden in the bottom of the rice can?

BING-HU: [*Laughs*] That was clever of you to hide the dollars, Little Sister!

ME-HWA: The Evil Uncle says he is our legal guardian and we must work for *him*.

BING-HU: I don't believe that he is our guardian. If we had a grandfather, we could prove it!

ME-HWA: We might adopt a grandfather.

MUSIC: *Up full with music.*

ME-HWA: The procession is over! Let's hurry home!

BING-HU: Not quite over! Now approaches the heavenly prince. We must not leave yet. We might be punished!

ME-HWA: Bing-hu! We must go at once! [*Alarmed*] Something is wrong! I feel that all is not well at home. Dea-dea! Liang-au! [*Gradually fading*] Dea-dea is in trouble! Dea-dea!—

SOUND: *Voices of Me-wha and Uncle cross fade.*

UNCLE: [*Snarling voice*] I tell you, woman! I'm their legal guardian! I am their next of kin!

LIANG-AU: I beg of you, Honorable Uncle, do not take little Dea-dea from his brother and sister!

UNCLE: Bah! I take the baby now! I come back for the Girl-Child and the Man-Child! I can sell workers for good money!

55

LIANG-AU: But these children do not want to go with you. They can earn their own living! They can buy their own rice!

UNCLE: [*Shouting*] Earn their own rice! I tell you I am their legal guardian! They must do what I say! It is the law of China, Old Woman!

LIANG-AU: If you wish to care for them, why do you take Dea-dea now?

UNCLE: [*Insinuatingly*] He is a handsome boy! A rich person will pay well for so handsome a boy. [*Gloatingly*] Will pay very well for so beautiful a boy!

SOUND: *Dea-dea cries. U-see barks.*

LIANG-AU: [*In misery*] No! No! You must not sell Dea-dea!

SOUND: *Dea-dea continues to cry and U-see to bark.*

UNCLE: Get out of my way, Old Woman! Take that, you cur!

SOUND: *U-see gives whelp of pain and whines.*

MUSIC: *Up full with music.*

SOUND: *Fade in sound of approaching footsteps.*

ME-HWA: [*Fading in*] Bing-hu, from here, the lanterns look like stars from the rainbow. Soon I shall see the lights of our sampan! Please walk faster!

SOUND: *Footsteps faster. Keep under.*

BING-HU: Slower, sister! I'm stiff from sitting on the pier.

ME-HWA: I almost wish we had not left Dea-dea so long.

BING-HU: The Demon Chaser has given you bad thoughts, Sister.

ME-HWA: Now I see our little sampan! Look! Bing-hu, someone swings a lantern! [*Questioningly*] Can it be Liang-au signaling to us? We must hurry!

SOUND: *Running footsteps.*

BING-HU: We're almost there!

ME-HWA: [*Breathless*] Can something have happened to Dea-dea? [*Calls*] Liang-au! Liang-au, is Dea-dea all right?

LIANG-AU: [*Fade in voice and sobbing*] Your uncle, the Evil One, took Dea-dea! He says he is your guardian! He says he has a right!

BING-HU: I do not believe he is our real uncle! Our father scarcely knew him!

ME-HWA: We're Dea-dea's big people! The Evil One is not our Uncle!

LIANG-AU: The Evil One says he will take you too—I tried to stop him! If you only had a grandfather! Then the Evil Uncle could not take you!

BING-HU: What is he going to do with Dea-dea?

LIANG-AU: The Evil One says he will sell Dea-dea to rich folks! He says rich folks will pay much silver for a baby boy so beautiful and strong.

BING-HU: He won't dare! That old Pock-face! That mean Old Wrapped-in-straw! I'll—I'll—

ME-HWA: What can we do, Bing-hu?

BING-HU: Don't cry, Me-hwa! We'll find Dea-dea! Let's go inside now!

SOUND: *Footsteps. Door opening and closing.*

ME-HWA: I'll light the incense before Ma-chu, Queen of Heaven.

SOUND: *Scratching of match.*

ME-HWA: There! [*Prays*] Grandmother Ma-chu, beloved goddess of sailors and river people, save Dea-dea. Please save Dea-dea!

BING-HU: We will get him back, Me-hwa. I'm strong. Feel my muscle!

SOUND: *Whimpering of dog heard again. Fading in.*

ME-HWA: Look! It's U-see! Our little puppy! Oh, his leg is hurt!

BING-HU: Come, U-see! Let me look at your leg! [*Dog whines*] He's been kicked! Bring the bandages!

ME-HWA: I'll bring them. I bet U-see followed Dea-dea and the Evil One kicked him!

BING-HU: The cruel fox! To kick a little dog!

ME-HWA: Poor little puppy. [*Dog barks*] There, U-see! We'll bandage your leg! Tonight, you may sleep near Dea-dea's little duck! [*U-see barks contentedly*] I'll make your bed near by. Tomorrow, we shall find Dea-dea!

SOUND: *Dog barks! Duck quacks. Gradually fade.*

MUSIC: *Musical curtain.*

ANNOUNCER: Now it is the next day. Since dawn, Bing-hu and Me-hwa have rowed their little sampan up and down and across the River Min, Bright and Shining

River. But their eyes cannot see the green fields where the Min flows, for Dea-dea, Little Gold and Precious Jewels has not been found.

SOUND: *Fade in sound of oars in water and voice of Bing-hu.*

BING-HU: It's like hunting a flea in a straw mattress. All day we have shuttled back and forth and up and down —above the Big Bridge and below the Big Bridge—but no sight of Uncle's sampan.

ME-HWA: Let's go far down the River Min—where the big ships anchor.

BING-HU: Maybe we can pick up some passengers. Uncle will be looking for passengers! Keep watching for his sampan! [*Calls*] Sung-i-ang!—Little Boat! Sung-i-ang!

ME-HWA: See that big black steamer that's just arrived!

BING-HU: Yes! We'll go there! There may be passengers to ferry! [*Calls*] Sung-i-ang!

ME-HWA: S-sh! Don't call! Isn't that Uncle's bright colored sampan tied along side the steamboat?

BING-HU: No doubt about it!

ME-HWA: Do you think that Dea-dea might be there?

BING-HU: That's what we shall find out! I think we can hide behind that junk in the river near the steamboat.

ME-HWA: [*Low voice*] You're pulling in nicely, Bing-hu! I am sure the Evil One has not seen us!

BING-HU: Crouch low! Uncle is moving heavy baskets and chests! He must have a passenger!

ME-HWA: [*Excitedly*] Bing-hu! Kneel here! Look! I see Dea-dea! He's back of the stern oar! See his little pigtails bobbing!

BING-HU: [*Anxiously*] I see him! He's climbing rather high!

ME-HWA: S-sh! Now I hear Aunt scolding him—

AUNT: [*Fading in*] But I tell you—you good for nothing—

UNCLE: [*On mike*] I told you—we'll sell the boy-child first! He'll bring a good sum!

AUNT: Ai! Ai! Glad I'll be to be rid of him too!

UNCLE: We must find the other two. The man-child is strong. He can row our boat and earn much silver for us! You can care for the girl-child for a time.

AUNT: [*Angry*] Not for the little silver that we can get for her puny pack of bones will I enter that sampan of theirs!

UNCLE: Coward! What do you wish *me* to do with her?

AUNT: I have talked to Lau-po, seller of slave girls!

UNCLE: Ai—what did Lau-po say?

AUNT: Lau-po says the girl-child has a lily face, but most persons prefer them with more fat on their skeletons!

UNCLE: Then Lau-po does not want the girl-child?

AUNT: Oh, she will take her! She'll get rid of her!

UNCLE: Be sure Lau-po pays you a good price. [*Voice fading. Dead air for a few seconds*]

ME-HWA: [*Fading in*] What do the Evil Ones mean?

BING-HU: They plan to sell you and Dea-dea, and keep me to work for them!

ME-HWA: [*Cries*] Oh, Bing-hu! They already have Dea-dea!

BING-HU: Courage, little sister! We're going to get Dea-dea!—

ME-HWA: I wish Dea-dea would not climb so high! He will fall into the water!

BING-HU: [*Excitedly*] Fall into the water!—yes!—just that!—fall into the water!—let him fall! Then I'll swim under the water and catch him!

ME-HWA: [*In awe*] Bing-hu! And you can swim like a fish!

BING-HU: Here! Let me have that rope! Now, Me-hwa, you steer our sampan down stream and in behind that steamboat! [*Pause*] There! Stop! That's fine!

ME-HWA: If only the Evil Ones do not see us! But I think we are where they cannot see us.

BING-HU: I'll quack like Dea-dea's duck! [*He quacks like duck*]

ME-HWA: Dea-dea hears you! He holds out his arms! He's lost his balance! He's falling! [*Splash as Dea-dea hits water*] Swim, Bing-hu, swim! What long strokes Bing-hu takes! Now he swims under the water! Ma-chu be thanked! Bing-hu has Dea-dea by the shoulders! Now they swim toward our sampan! Ma-chu, friend of boatmen, don't let the Evil Ones see Bing-hu and Dea-dea!

SOUND: *Voice of Me-hwa cross fades with that of Uncle.*

UNCLE: Where's that child?

AUNT: [*Bit concerned*] He can't be far!—perhaps he's fallen overboard!

SOUND: *Crash of falling boxes.*

61

UNCLE: But the boy would bring us money! [*More boxes fall. Uncle yells*] Pick up those boxes, you lazy woman! Why didn't you watch the boy? If he has fallen, we might be blamed for the accident.

AUNT: Nonsense! Every sampan has a child fall overboard now and then!

SOUND: *Another crash of falling boxes.*

UNCLE: Let's get out of here! I wonder where that man-child is hiding—[*Voice fading*]

SOUND: *Dead air for few seconds. Fade in sound of Bing-hu sputtering and blowing water from his mouth and nose.*

BING-HU: We made it! Didn't we, Dea-dea?

ME-HWA: Dea-dea, Gold and Precious Jewels! Dea-dea and Bing-hu—both safe on our little sampan!

BING-HU: That was the best swim I have had for a long time!

DEA-DEA: Dea-dea swim! Bing-hu swim! Two people swim!

BING-HU: [*Concerned*] The oars! We must hurry away from here! The cruel ones might see us!

ME-HWA: I am sure we are hidden! The roof of their sampan blocks their view. But we must get away! We shall go far away and look for passengers—somewhere where the Evil Uncle will not look for us!

BING-HU: We shall have to hide Dea-dea inside the boat when there are people around.

ME-HWA: Dea-dea will have to be quiet as a fish under water.

62

DEA-DEA: Dea-dea like to be quiet as fish under water!

BING-HU: Just let Old Wrapped-in-straw try to take Dea-dea from us again!

ME-HWA: Look, Bing-hu! We're passing by the Big Learning Hall on the hill. Let us go to the Good-to-Love Lady! She will tell us what to do!

BING-HU: And one day, we shall begin to read books there! The River Min will yet bring us good fortune!

ME-HWA: The Min, Bright and Shining River,
And the fields that are green where she flows.

BING-HU: [*Calls happily*] Sung-i-ang! Little Boat! Sung-i-ang!— [*Voice gradually fades*]

MUSIC: *Up and end with music.*

Pied Piper of Hamelin

From the *Pied Piper of Hamelin,* by Robert Browning. Adapted for radio by Katherine Watson. (Grades 3, 4-5) 5 minutes

CAST OF CHARACTERS

PIED PIPER
MAYOR OF HAMELIN
FIVE TOWNSPEOPLE
EIGHT COUNCILMEN
CHILDREN
HANS .... the lame boy

SOUNDS

Footsteps
Tap on door
Door opening

Bells ringing
Piper's pipe

Pied Piper of Hamelin

ANNOUNCER: This story is laid in Germany with the Mayor and Council seated at a table—townspeople are all very angry—listen!

TOWNSPEOPLE: Rats, rats!

MAYOR: There, there! my good people. How can we understand you if you all shout at once? Speak out one at a time, and tell us the trouble.

1ST TOWNSMAN: [*Angrily*] Aye—aye—we'll tell. It's told in one word. Rats.

MAYOR: Rats!

2ND TOWNSMAN: Yes rats. They bite the babies in the cradles.

3RD TOWNSMAN: They fight the dogs and kill the cats.

4TH TOWNSMAN: And eat the cheeses out of the vats.

5TH TOWNSMAN: They make nests inside men's Sunday hats.

MAYOR: Well! What do you expect us to do?

1ST TOWNSMAN: We expect you to rid this town of rats.

MAYOR: But how, my good people?

2ND TOWNSMAN: That is for you to find out. Rouse up, for you must think of a remedy!

3RD TOWNSMAN: Yes, clear this town of rats, or we'll put others in your place.

4TH TOWNSMAN: Let's go and let them think of a plan.

SOUND: *Footsteps—fading out.*

MAYOR: Well, what can we do? I've thought and thought until my poor head aches, and not a bit of good has it done me.

SOUND: *Light tapping at door.*

MAYOR: Gracious, what is that?

1ST COUNCILMAN: It sounded like the scraping of feet on the mat. There must be somebody at the door.

MAYOR: Oh! it frightened me—for I thought it was a rat; and the very sound makes my heart go pit-a-pat. Come in!

SOUND: *Door opening and footsteps approaching.*

MAYOR: [*In a low voice*] What a strange looking, tall fellow! Look at the pipe around his neck. [*Louder*] Who are you?

PIED PIPER: I am called the Pied Piper.

MAYOR: Oh! go away. We are in such great trouble, we have no time to listen to music.

PIED PIPER: Please, your honor, I *do* know what troubles you and I have come to help you.

MAYOR and COUNCILMEN: Help us! How?

PIED PIPER: Do you see my pipe? It is a magic pipe. On it I can blow music that will charm every creature under the sun, even rats. If I charm away your rats, will you give me one thousand gilders?

MAYOR and COUNCILMEN: A thousand gilders? Rid this town of rats and we will give you fifty thousand gilders!

PIED PIPER: Then come!

66

MUSIC: *Bridge.*

ANNOUNCER: The Mayor and Council follow the Pied Piper from the room. They soon reach the street. The Piper walks along, blowing his pipe; the rats follow, running.

SOUND: *Playing of Piper's magic pipe.*

1ST COUNCILMAN: Look! look! Out of the houses the rats come tumbling.

2ND COUNCILMAN: Great rats—small rats, lean rats, brawny rats, brown rats, black rats, gray rats, tawny rats.

3RD COUNCILMAN: Grave old plodders, spry young friskers.

4TH COUNCILMAN: Fathers, mothers, uncles, cousins, cocking tails and pricking whiskers.

5TH COUNCILMAN: Families by tens and dozens, brothers, sisters, husbands, wives, follow the Piper for their lives.

6TH COUNCILMAN: From street to street he pipes advancing, And step by step they follow dancing,

7TH COUNCILMAN: They are at the River Weser.

8TH COUNCILMAN: Very brave, all plunged in and perished.

SOUND: *Great rejoicing—bells ringing—people crying hurrah! hurrah!*

MAYOR: You see, good people, your mayor and council did help you. See how we've rid the town of rats!

1ST TOWNSMAN: True, true—long live the mayor and council!

67

SOUND: *Approaching footsteps.*

PIED PIPER: Now, if you please, my thousand gilders.

MAYOR: A thousand gilders!

COUNCILMEN: A thousand gilders! Must we pay this fellow a thousand gilders?

MAYOR: Come, come, my good fellow—that was all a joke. Come, take fifty!

PIED PIPER: You'll give me a thousand gilders as you promised, or you'll be sorry—I know another tune that I play when people make me angry.

MAYOR: What! Do you think we are afraid of a wandering piper? What harm can you do? The rats are drowned—you can't frighten us—blow your pipe till you burst.

ANNOUNCER: The piper, with pipe raised to his lips, moves slowly down the street. This time the children follow him.

SOUND: *Piper's pipe—footsteps—children.*

TOWNSPEOPLE: Our children, our children! He is leading them to the river. He will drown them. Oh! call him back. See! They have reached the mountain side.

1ST TOWNSMAN: Oh, look! A door has opened and our children have followed the Piper into the mountain. See, the door is closing!

2ND TOWNSMAN: Oh! our children. We shall never see our children again.

SOUND: *Child crying.*

3RD TOWNSMAN: Hush, I hear a child crying. Why, it's Hans, the little boy who's lame.

HANS: Oh, dear! I want to go with the other children.

1ST TOWNSMAN: Go with the other children! Don't you know the wicked Piper has shut all the other children in the mountain?

HANS: He is not a wicked Piper, and the children are not shut in the mountain. The kind Piper is leading them to a beautiful land. The door in the mountain leads to that land. There the sky is always blue, and there are beautiful flowers, and the sweetest birds sing. There the people are never sick and never sad, and no one is lame. But I could not run as fast as the other children, and so I am shut out.

2ND TOWNSMAN: That beautiful land must be fairyland. Our children will be happy there, and they will never be sick nor sad.

MAYOR: No—but we shall always be sad. We have broken our promise, and the children have left us. But, friends, let us be glad that they are safe and happy forever in the beautiful land of the fairies.

The Singing Tree

15 minutes

CAST OF CHARACTERS

JANCSI .... Hungarian boy of thirteen
KATE .... girl of same age, cousin of Jancsi
FATHER ⎫
        ⎬ .... Jancsi's parents
MOTHER ⎭
CLERK IN THE TOWN HALL

SOUNDS

Rattle of paper	Horses' hoofs
Creaking of wagon	Rattle of dishes
Footsteps	Music

The Singing Tree

ANNOUNCER: The scene of *The Singing Tree* is laid in a little village of Hungary. The time is June 1914. We find Jancsi, a boy of thirteen, and his cousin Kate, a girl of the same age, living on a farm several miles away from the village.

Our scene opens with Jancsi and Kate in Uncle Moses' general store in the village.

JANCSI: Now we're in for it. We shouldn't have stayed so long in Uncle Moses' shop. Let's get home, or Father will forget that I'm thirteen years old and give me more than a look.

KATE: Yes, you're right—we must go. Please hurry and wrap up the red ribbons I've bought, Uncle Moses.

SOUND: *Rattle of paper.*

ANNOUNCER: The yard was dark and quiet when the wagon approached the farmhouse.

SOUND: *Creaking of wagon.*

ANNOUNCER: Jancsi's father was standing in the doorway. we hear him say—

FATHER: Jancsi, wash your hands and finish milking. Get going!

JANCSI: Yes, Father. We were late because we stopped to look at that old monument by the road.

FATHER: That's something all Hungarian children should remember. And, Kate, your aunt needs help in the kitchen.

71

KATE: Yes, Uncle Márton.

FATHER: You'll have to hurry, for it's almost suppertime.

MOTHER: Don't be angry with them!

FATHER: Well, it seems my whole family is against me. What am I, a dragon? Come on and eat your supper. But remember, son, you are a farmer. Leaving your job in the corn wasn't so bad. But the first thing a poor farmer learns is that when milking time comes, a cow isn't interested in excuses, good or bad. All a cow wants is to be milked.

JANCSI: Then I'm glad we're not raising cows.

MOTHER: What's wrong with cows?

JANCSI: Nothing. They are—well, they're just cows, that's all. Horses are different. You can ride them, train them, talk to them.

FATHER: Spoken like a good horseman, Jancsi.

JANCSI: You mean that, Father? You mean I'm a good horseman?

FATHER: Yes, I think you are good enough to have your own herd.

JANCSI: Thank you, Father. That would mean a lot to me. I'll breed the best horses on the plains—proud, high-stepping white horses—and get you a golden coach, Mother, and a velvet gown heavy with gold and diamonds and rubies.

MOTHER: Oh, Jan, what a sweet thought.

JANCSI: You will look like a queen; and I will take you riding all over the plains, into the towns and cities, and everywhere people will stop and look and ask, "Who is this beautiful queen?" And I will crack my whip and shout, "She is my mother."

KATE: You forgot something.

JANCSI: What?

KATE: Us.

JANCSI: No, I didn't either, but I guess we'd better leave you home with your chickens.

KATE: That's all right with me. I like it here. I can raise thousands of chickens so they'll lay millions of eggs, and I'll sell them; and when I have enough money, I'll buy one of those American tractors for Uncle Márton.

FATHER: No, not for me. I'll disown you, Kate, if you even speak of those noisy, smelling brutes.

MOTHER: I feel the same way, Father; but machinery will come to the plains sooner or later.

FATHER: I know, but I also know our people. Before they give up their peaceful, unhurried ways, their very souls will have to be changed.

MOTHER: What could change them?

FATHER: A war could. Yes, a war could destroy their dignity, their good nature, their contentment. But this is 1914. Two generations have grown up in peace; become used to thinking of people in other countries as brothers, not enemies. What would anybody start a war for? Why, our men would just laugh and go back to their plowing!

MOTHER: Granted that you are right. And now, how about going to bed? We'll have to get up early if we all go to Peter's wedding tomorrow.

SOUND: *Footsteps—fade.*

ANNOUNCER: That was two months ago. Since July 28th, when Austria-Hungary had declared war on Serbia every mail had brought news of more and more countries declaring war on one another—Russia against Austria-Hungary, Germany against France, England against Germany. Hungary was at war—not only Hungary—all of Europe. We overhear this conversation at the breakfast table.

MOTHER: Márton, with all the men away, what will we do? I live in fear. Any day one of those dreadful yellow cards might come—calling you in—taking you away. Márton, if I see that card, I will die.

FATHER: Now, now, old lady, that is no way to talk. I assure you, Mother, that none of those yellow cards will come into our house. Now smile!

MOTHER: You mean—they won't take you?

FATHER: Bah! Nobody can take me anywhere. I go where I want to go or have to go, but take me? No!

JANCSI: I will, if you sit here gossiping much longer.

FATHER: Are the horses ready?

JANCSI: Hours ago.

FATHER: Well, then we'd better be off, son. We won't start haying today. We'll ride into town. I have some things to do that can't wait.

JANCSI: Oh! if I had known we were going to change our plans, I would have worn my blue suit. Maybe we'll eat in one of those restaurants.

FATHER: You look all right.

SOUND: *Horses' hoofs.*

ANNOUNCER: And now Jancsi and his father have reached town. It was all very wonderful to Jancsi; for he had been to the village only three times in his life. They

74

stopped at the Town Hall first; and to Jancsi's surprise, the clerk was expecting them. We hear the clerk who says:

CLERK: So this is the young fellow!

FATHER: Young, but level headed. He'll be all right.

CLERK: Humph! Too bad—this war. Just sign this—both of you.

JANCSI: But what is it, Father?

FATHER: I'll explain, son. This paper gives you the right to buy or sell anything on the farm—animals, grain, food—whatever we need, without asking me first. You know how busy we are now. Sometimes I may not be home when the buyers come, and this will save time.

JANCSI: You mean I can do anything you would do?

FATHER: Practically.

JANCSI: When—gimme that pen. Wait till I tell Kate—and Mother. Whew!

FATHER: Well, that's that! Now hang onto this paper.

JANCSI: Don't worry, I'll sleep with it under my pillow.

FATHER: How about a great big meal now, son? Make us feel better.

JANCSI: Oh! Can I have all the ice cream I want for once without Mother worrying about stomach aches?

FATHER: Well, let's not worry about a little thing like a stomach ache. War is a much bigger thing.

JANCSI: I hate it.

FATHER: We all do. But do you remember the round-up, Jancsi, when you and Kate got caught in a stampede?

JANCSI: Do I!

FATHER: Well, war is like a stampede, Jancsi. A small thing can start it and suddenly the very earth is shaking with fury. People turn into wild things, crushing everything beautiful and sweet, blindly destroying homes and lives in their mad rush from nowhere to nowhere. A stampede, a mad whirlwind that sucks in men like those marching so bravely.

JANCSI: But I hate it, Father.

FATHER: Everybody hates it; but we're caught in a stampede and we'll have to see it through.

SOUND: *Rattle of dishes.*

JANCSI: Oh! I've eaten so much I can hardly get up from the chair.

FATHER: Well, then, stay where you are. I have to do some things anyway; wait for me here, son.

ANNOUNCER: Jancsi looked at some magazines while waiting for his father, who has now returned; and this is what we hear—

JANCSI: Father, what are you wearing?

FATHER: It's my uniform, son.

JANCSI: Uniform?

FATHER: Yes, Corporal Márton Nagy of the 7th Infantry. I have but half an hour before leaving. Come, son, chin up, young fellow. This is the castor oil.

JANCSI: You knew—all day you knew!

FATHER: I've known it for quite a while, son. What I didn't want was anyone crying over me. That's why I didn't tell.

MUSIC: *Musical curtain.*

76

ANNOUNCER: Márton Nagy goes to the front and Jancsi carries on the affairs at home. Six big Russian prisoners arrive and work hard on the farm. Relatives and friends find it a haven with Mother Nagy and Kate endeavoring to keep high hearts in spite of worry about husband and father at the front. The months pass wearily on. Then begins a period of anxiety, waiting in vain for news from the front. For two years Jancsi is the master on the Nagy ranch; and then suddenly Father is home, because he has been wounded in the war and is not able to go back. We hear the father and mother talking.

FATHER: Mother, it says here in the paper that children are without milk and nourishing food. The government is issuing a plea to farmers to take as many children as they can feed. Children are the most hopeless sufferers in the war. We have a large house. Do you suppose we could?

MOTHER: Take some children? Once we had a small family; but now we have a large house and a large family, and it will be still larger. I would feed an army of hungry children if we could.

FATHER: Let's start with five—that's a lucky number. Five young kittens have come to us; we will give each of them a child to play with. Five children then, Mother?

MOTHER: Six, Márton, please. One for each kitten and one for Baby Panni.

FATHER: That makes how many additions to a small family? You count.

MOTHER: Kate, Sándor, Lily, her mother, the six Russian prisoners, Mari and her baby, Grandma, Grandpa, and six children to come. Twenty!

FATHER: Don't forget the three dogs and I don't know how many kittens. Quite a houseful. Tomorrow I shall ride into town and make out the papers. Shall I ask for three of each kind, boys and girls?

MOTHER: Yes. Then Jancsi can teach the boys to ride.

ANNOUNCER: And so the refugee children arrive to be nursed back to health. Everything is strange to them at first, but they are soon quite at home and find the farm a haven. On Christmas Eve, the fourth Christmas of the war, the old kitchen glowed once more with candles on the tree, their mellow light shining onto many more faces than ever before. But Christmas and succeeding months have gone by very quickly, and now it is April. Let's listen in while Mother says—

MOTHER: How time flies! Don't you think so, Kate?

KATE: There are so many ways to count time now. All of us count it by something different. All except you, Auntie. You—oh, I'm all mixed up now.

FATHER: I don't think you are mixed up, Kate. I think I know what you are thinking about and it's time somebody put it into words. Let me tell you a story. It will be a war story again. It begins with guns booming and shells screaming, but it will end with the words you were thinking. This story began one day in August 1915. We had been advancing all night—through the long, silent night that followed a day of the heaviest shellfire from both sides, the Russians' and ours. Each had been trying to advance. Finally the Russians left their trenches and retreated. After sundown we were ordered to follow their retreat. We marched, or rather crept and stumbled, across this no-man's land of shell holes, barbed wire, burned-down forests, ruined houses, and deserted Russian gun-nets. Except for us, there was nothing alive anywhere. All night we crept and stumbled.

KATE: And what happened then?

FATHER: Then, when men's teeth began to chatter with fear, a finger of light, a tiny weak herald of the approaching dawn, shone on the edge of the darkness. "Dawn," a creeping man said, as if he had never hoped to see a dawn again. And then, as the sun broke through the clouds at last, we saw one tree, one single apple tree that must have been near a house, only the house was no longer there. "It is alive," the man said, as if he never had hoped to see a green tree again. "It sings," someone whispered. "It is alive; I can hear it."

MUSIC: *Soft music in distance.*

KATE: Oh, Uncle! And then what?

FATHER: Men rose to their feet and walked and ran toward the singing tree, which was alive with birds,—living birds singing to the dawn in a live apple tree. Here they were—small, feathered orphans of a man-made storm, singing to the dawn. The one live thing that would never go away unless a man-made gun should uproot it from the earth it grew in, was the apple tree. Small orphans—large ones—for a while found shelter on its sturdy limbs. They would pass on. New ones might come. There might be storms again. But you, Mother of all, like the tree, will remain the same.

MUSIC: *Musical curtain.*

ANNOUNCER: Everywhere the eyes of men, women and children were turning toward the same light of hope. The prayers for peace in people's hearts lent it a radiance it never really had. So the war came to an end. Father and Jancsi drove into the village that day for the news. On the way home, when they reached the lane, Jancsi touched his father's arm and we hear—

79

JANCSI: Could we stop for a moment, Father? I would like to see if it is still there. I mean the tree—the monument.

FATHER: If it isn't, son, you and I will carve a new one, for the next generation to see.

JANCSI: Oh! there it is.

FATHER: Four years of storm haven't marred the deeply carved words that have withstood the storms of half a century. It says: Liberty, equality, fraternity. The month of March 1848. And underneath, the list of names beginning with your great-grandfather, Márton Nagy, the large landowner, and ending with Moses Mandelbaum, the small Jewish merchant. Soon these beautiful words will ring again all over the world. Only a fourth one, just born, will ring again clearer. *Peace.* Please God. Just peace.

JANCSI: You know what, Father?

FATHER: What, son?

JANCSI: That story about the singing tree—remember?

FATHER: U-hum.

JANCSI: Well, I know what you meant about Mother and how she is always the same—and I like the way you said the story for her. But—but to me—the singing tree was more than—more than even Mother. To me—

FATHER: Yes?

JANCSI: To me, the stillness and the ruins in the story were the—was the time when—you weren't here. And the tree—it's the house and you and Mother—it's everything we are, sort of together. Aw—you know what I mean—

FATHER: Yes, I do, son. Small orphans, big ones, for a while found shelter—

80

JANCSI: They would pass on—

FATHER: New ones might come. There might be storms again, but—

JANCSI: But we, the house and us, we would remain the same.

An Ear for Uncle Emil

Adapted from *An Ear for Uncle Emil,* by Eva R. Gaggin. Copyright 1939 by E. R. Gaggin and Kate Seredy. Used by special arrangement with The Viking Press, Inc. All rights reserved. This play may not be reproduced in any form, or performed publicly or broadcast, except by written permission of The Viking Press, 18 East 48th Street, New York 17, N.Y. Adapted for radio by Katherine Watson. (Grades 5-6)   15 minutes

CAST OF CHARACTERS

RESI .... a little girl

PETER .... boy, same age

GRANDMOTHER .... Resi's grandmother

SEPP GUTZBERGER .... toy shop owner

MR. OBEREGG .... toymaker

ANGELA .... girl younger than Resi

SOUNDS

Footsteps   Knock at door
Door opening   Drawer opening
Door closing   Music

An Ear for Uncle Emil

ANNOUNCER: Come with me to Middlemeadow and meet Resi Witt, the most amazing, the gayest little girl that has come out of Switzerland for a long time. She belongs to the Marching Mountain Maids Accordian Unit; and Uncle Emil, a herdsman doll, is her proudest possession. Uncle Emil is much the worse for wear. Gigi, the goose, has pecked away first one thing and then another, and even his pants are glued on. But Resi thinks of her doll, Uncle Emil, as part of her own family.

Our scene opens with Resi Witt sitting under a linden tree, with the mountains in the background of her pretty pink house. We hear her talking with Peter, who lives next door.

RESI: Oh! there's no place as nice as the Mountain Meadows in Switzerland. People who belong on them can never be happy anywhere else. They miss the flowery slopes and the cunning little houses—and there's— -

PETER: Goats—you're forgetting about the goats, Resi. There's more goats here than anything else.

RESI: I was forgetting them on purpose. Think I don't want a little rest from them sometimes? What are you doing over here, Peter?

PETER: Looking for Edelweiss, that good-for-nothing goat. She's run away again.

RESI: Well! that's good. Maybe she will be so kind as to stay away this time.

PETER: Oh! look over there; you can see Roggi's place. Our neighbor, Otto Biel's mother, was telling us a lot about Angela Roggi down in church this morning; or I mean after church.

RESI: What did she say, Peter?

PETER: She told how the dreadful avalanche had crippled Angela and killed her father and mother and about how Angela has to leave Highmeadow.

RESI: Leave Highmeadow! Why?

PETER: Cause how can she live up there in a wheel chair, silly? When a person's lame, they've got to live where it's flat; don't you see?

RESI: Is Angela going to be lame always?

PETER: Maybe. There's nobody on Highmeadow can take care of her, so she has to live down mountain with an old aunty; and she cries all the time about having to leave the high mountains. Mrs. Biel is collecting presents for Angela and she wanted us to tell you to go down mountain and see her just as soon as you could. Look! Here comes your old goose back, and if she isn't bringing Uncle Emil with her! There, she dropped him on the bottom step. You'd better get him.

RESI: Oh! dear—just look at him! Every time I hide this doll, no matter where, that old goose, Gigi, finds him and pecks something more off him.

PETER: There's not much left to Uncle Emil any more, is there?

RESI: [*In a hurt voice*] Oh! how can you say that? Uncle Emil is the best herdsman doll on this meadow, Peter Kirchli; and don't you ever forget it!

PETER: Mrs. Biel says that we should all bring Angela some toy for her to take down the mountain. We may even have to sacrifice something we ourselves love. What will you take, Resi?

RESI: I'll give her my best handerchief with embroidery on it.

PETER: No, Mrs. Biel wants you to give Uncle Emil to Angela.

RESI: [*Shrieks*] Uncle Emil! Why, Peter Kirchli, Uncle Emil is part of the family!

PETER: Oh, look there on the ground. Gigi just pecked off Uncle Emil's last ear. Well! if that isn't Edelweiss over there. I knew I'd find her if I kept right on looking. Good-by, Resi. I must run and catch her.

SOUND: *Footsteps.*

RESI: Oh! Uncle Emil, you do look worn. You haven't any buttons on your pants. No arms, no nose, no hair. Suppose Angela should slap my Uncle Emil into a corner and—and 'spise him, just 'cause he's old and shabby. I wouldn't want for Uncle Emil to be 'spised. He's got to be loved always. Suppose now—just suppose I could get an ear for Uncle Emil—Oh! I must ask Grandmother Resi. [*Calling*] Grandmother Resi—I have to ask you a question.

SOUND: *Door opening and closing.*

GRANDMOTHER: Have you got yourself in trouble again, Resi?

RESI: Not me. Uncle Emil.

GRANDMOTHER: What's wrong with our herdsman doll?

RESI: His ear. It's just a hole now. Gigi pecked it.

GRANDMOTHER: Well, let it go. With all the other things that Uncle Emil has lost here and there, nobody is going to fuss over a mere ear.

RESI: But Angela Roggi might—if she didn't like holes. She might think he was trash and throw him out in the street.

GRANDMOTHER: So! I begin to see. Now start at the beginning and tell me all about it.

RESI: Well, Angela has to leave Highmeadow and the goats—and live with her aunty in the village; and she is crying all the time.

GRANDMOTHER: It's too bad she has to leave. But what has all this to do with Uncle Emil's ear?

RESI: Well, Mrs. Biel said she wanted us all to give Angela something we treasured—so she wants me to give her Uncle Emil.

SOUND: *Knock at door.*

GRANDMOTHER: Come in! Why it's Sepp Gutzberger. It's little Sepp, but grown up.

SEPP: Don't ever think it. It's still the grubby lad who was forever chasing his dog up these flowery slopes.

GRANDMOTHER: Sepp—Sepp. Handsomer with every passing year. The mountains can well boast when they send lads like you across the water. Now tell us about your toy shop in America.

SEPP: I *am* proud of my toy shop. I've just ordered two hundred herdsmen and mountain maid dolls from the five men who make dolls here in Toymaker Street.

GRANDMOTHER: It's good to have you here if it is only for this one summer. How does it seem to be back again?

86

SEPP: Oh! it's wonderful. The things you miss when you leave home are not the flowery mountains, but your own childhood; and that's not so easy to find again. But I'm going to—don't think I'm not.

GRANDMOTHER: How are you going to do this, Sepp?

SEPP: I'm going to have fun up and down these flowery slopes.

GRANDMOTHER: I well remember when you were a boy, Sepp, and had fun—other children had fun with you. You were a happy child only when you were making others happy.

SEPP: I think what would please me most now would be to find some unhappy child and make her as happy as I was in the long ago.

GRANDMOTHER: And I know just how you can do it. Angela Roggi has been made an orphan and a cripple by an avalanche that killed her father and mother.

SEPP: What could I do for her?

GRANDMOTHER: There's a wonderful hospital in Zurich and skilled doctors who say that Angela could be operated on successfully to cure her lameness.

SEPP: That would indeed make me very happy.

MUSIC: *Musical curtain.*

ANNOUNCER: It is now the next day. Resi has gone down the mountain and is now at Emil Oberegg's toy shop.

SOUND: *Knock on door. Door opens—then closes.*

RESI: Hello, I came to get an—an—maybe two ears for Uncle Emil.

Mr. Oberegg: Who is your Uncle Emil?

Resi: He's a herdsman doll.

Mr. Oberegg: Good heavens, a doll!

Resi: The reason he looks so queer is because our old goose, Gigi, pecked him. The hair isn't really his. Some of it is Miz's tail, and some came from the cows. That patch right there was a bit of Edelweiss' whiskers—she's the goat next door.

Mr. Oberegg: If Uncle Emil belonged to me, I should feed what's left of him to Gigi, the goose, and have a new doll.

Resi: Oh! but I couldn't—he's Uncle Emil. And besides, Angela Roggi, the little lame girl, has to have a herds-man doll. The children are going to give her something to remember the mountains by, and I'm going to give her Uncle Emil. Peter said maybe Angela would cry more at the way Uncle Emil looks now, so I thought he should have a new ear over the hole there. I have a whole crock of butter to pay you.

Mr. Oberegg: Well! What this doll needs is a whole new head—new ears, new eyes, new nose, new hair—everything.

Resi: Would you care, Mr. Oberegg, if I looked at some of your dolls? Don't you ever make heads with long golden hair?

Mr. Oberegg: Long golden hair? Curls, do you mean?

Resi: Maybe you couldn't make a head like Paula's new doll.

Mr. Oberegg: No? Was it something like this?

Sound: *Drawer opening.*

88

RESI: [*Gasps*] What—what's that? Where did you get it?

MR. OBEREGG: Get it? I made it. It's the finest doll that ever came out of my shop, and it's for Sepp Gutzberger. You know he has a toy shop of his own in America and has come back to the mountains for the summer.

RESI: That's the very head I have been looking for.

MR. OBEREGG: Oh, that's not a head for a herdsman doll.

RESI: But it's the one I want.

MR. OBEREGG: You want? How about Uncle Emil? What would he do with curls?

RESI: Oh, he'd manage. I'd tie them under his hat.

MR. OBEREGG: How about Angela Roggi, then?

RESI: Maybe she knows a cheesemaker with golden hair. You never can tell. Couldn't you make another head for Sepp Gutzberger, Mr. Oberegg?

MR. OBEREGG: Yes, easily.

RESI: Then please go ahead and fasten this one on to Uncle Emil's shoulders. I—I love it.

MR. OBEREGG: All right, then. I'll snip Uncle Emil's old head off and surprise him with a new one. Won't he be a surprised man? Only I must say I'm shocked.

RESI: I'm not. Only I wish I had some ribbon to tie up Uncle Emil's curls.

MR. OBEREGG: Oh, my! Oh, my! A herdsman with his golden curls tied up on top of his head fifty years ago would have scared the cows. There's a bit of blue velvet ribbon in the drawer, if you must have it.

RESI: Oh, thank you, Mr. Oberegg. Isn't he the sweetest thing? I'll have to go now, and thank you ever so much. Good-by.

MUSIC: *Musical curtain.*

RESI: We're home at last, Uncle Emil. I wonder where Grandmother is?

GRANDMOTHER: Resi, Resi. Is that you? Come here, I want to see your doll. [*Gasps*] Oh, what kind of a herdsman is that? Why, he has golden curls and a blue ribbon.

RESI: Mr. Oberegg really made it for Sepp Gutzberger but he's going to make him another just like it.

GRANDMOTHER: What will Angela Roggi say to a herdsman like that? I'm ashamed to let Mrs. Biel see the doll now.

RESI: Oh, dear! Maybe I thought too much of how I'd like Uncle Emil to look and too little of Angela Roggi. He needs—he needs—

GRANDMOTHER: What he needs is his old head back again. Even with all the kinds of hair that grow on Mountain Meadows glued to it, it was better than golden braids. Maybe later I can figure out something to make Uncle Emil look better again.

ANNOUNCER: And so Uncle Emil has a wonderful head complete with long golden curls. Though no one else will look at him now, Resi thinks he's wonderful. Then as she can afford it, a lovely pair of hands replace the old ones; and so by successive stages, Uncle Emil becomes Emilie, pride of the countryside, but with his identity preserved through all these changes. It is going to be hard for Resi to give up Uncle Emil, or Emilie; but if Angela has to live down mountain, she will need comfort of some sort.

Winter has come again to Middlemeadow, and we find Resi coming home after a trip down mountain. She and Peter have delivered their gifts for Angela's Christmas, Uncle Emil among them. We hear—

90

SOUND: *Door opens and closes.*

RESI: Hello. What! nobody here? My, but it seems lonesome. Why, everybody's gone somewhere. Even Uncle Emil, I mean Emilie. It's the first time in all my life I've come up mountain that Uncle Emil wasn't waiting for me.

SOUND: *Someone stirs.*

RESI: Why, what was that? I thought I heard something move on the old loom bench, but I guess I was imagining it.

ANGELA: No, you didn't imagine it, for I am here. Hello, Resi! This is Angela.

RESI: Why, Angela, how good it is to see you; and how pretty you look in all your new clothes! How did you get up mountain tonight?

ANGELA: Sepp brought me. Look, I took Uncle Emil, Emilie, I mean, out of Mrs. Biel's baskets and brought her back to you.

RESI: But why are you giving her back to me? Don't you like her?

ANGELA: She's beautiful. I love him—I mean her; but you do too, Resi. Your father thought maybe we could love her together.

RESI: But how can we, if you are going to live down mountain with your aunty?

ANGELA: But I won't be down there. Your father said that maybe you would like to have me live with you.

RESI: And I'll have you for a little sister to love? Are you going to live here always?

ANGELA: If maybe you're wanting a sister.

91

RESI: Want one—want a sister? Why, Angela Roggi, I've always wanted one.

ANGELA: And I can climb mountains with you now, for I can walk good as new, thanks to Sepp Gutzberger, who took me to the doctor for an operation.

RESI: Oh! how wonderful. What good times we'll have together! Come on, Angela, supper's ready.

Book Week

Circus Day

A Book Week play. Courtesy of the Young People's Department of the Milwaukee Public Library. (Grades 5-6)   12 minutes

CAST OF CHARACTERS

MR. CASTLE .... ringmaster of the circus
JIM .... small boy
BARKER
PINOCCHIO .... book character
ROBIN HOOD .... book character
CHORUS
KING ARTHUR .... book character
HEPATICA .... book character
PAUL BUNYAN .... book character
ALICE .... book character
WINNIE-THE-POOH .... book character
BILL CODY .... book character
LONE RANGER .... radio star

SOUNDS

Caliope music   War whoops
Vendor calls   Music
Crack of whip   Cowboy yells
Marching feet   Wild west show
Indian calls   Dog barks

95

Circus Day

MR. CASTLE: This is only the beginning, Jim—only the beginning. Tonight you're going to get the thrill of your young life.

JIM: You mean I'll see some other people from books I've read?

MR. CASTLE: [*Chuckles*] I should say so! Remember, I told you that we folks in books really do live.

JIM: Gosh! I can hardly wait! Where are the rest of them?

MR. CASTLE: Ah! That's the real surprise. You know we book people get lonely during the long nights in the library. So we pass the time in fun.

JIM: In fun?

MR. CASTLE: Yes, Jim, and tonight we're having a circus—some of your best friends will be in the show—all the rest you've read about will step out of the books to see the performance.

JIM: A circus! I've only seen *one* circus in my whole life, but I never forgot it!!

MR. CASTLE: Well, you'll remember this one, I promise—but look, Jim—and listen—hear them; they're getting ready to start the show. That's the barker's voice now!

BARKER: Come right over, for the big show goes on immediately.

SOUND: *Calliope music, vendor calls, etc.*

BARKER: Boys and girls—today we are presenting for the first time and for a limited engagement only—the "Greatest Show on the Face of the Earth"—a stupendous—gigantic and supercolossal spectacle staged solely for your enjoyment and fun. It's packed with thrills—chuck full of suspense—brimming over with laughs—*and*—best of all—the only ticket you need to the A.O.B.W. Circus is your Public Library card! You'll meet all your old friends today—Toby Tyler's coming in the minute the performance starts—why—Dr. Dolittle is out taking care of a sick tiger this very second—and your old pal, Pinocchio, the clown, is ready to make you laugh your heads off! But wait!—what's this—why Pinocchio, what's the idea of being out front before the show?

PINOCCHIO: Little Dog Toby's gone!

BARKER: Gone—what do you mean?

PINOCCHIO: He's been missing for two hours now—we can't find him any place; even Bill Cody has gone out to look for him.

BARKER: Don't worry, Pinocchio; that old Indian scout will find him if it's possible.

PINOCCHIO: Just the same, I'm afraid he's gone for good.

BARKER: Cheer up, we'll find him in time for his act. You help hunt around. I've got to get back to announcing the performance. [*Louder tone*] Well, boys and girls, this is a disappointment—we'll miss Little Dog Toby, and we can't present his act; but I must tell you more about what you can expect from the greatest show on earth! What a host of acquaintances you'll meet! Frank Buck, and I do mean "Bring-Em-Back-Alive" Buck—Hepatica, world's tallest girl—there's surprise after surprise waiting for you in the A.O.B.W. Circus. And—as an added feature, additional to the Show at staggering cost and effort, we will, after the main performance, present a Wild West Show for those of you who have read about men like Bill Cody, better known as Buffalo Bill. He'll be here in person—leather chaps, rowel spurs, ten-gallon sombrero and all! But unless we get into our seats under the big top, we'll be late for the show—so—let's get going, boys and girls—careful there—no crowding in the aisles. There's the ringmaster, youngsters. What a sight!—hear him crack that long black whip!

SOUND: *Whip crack.*

BARKER: He's ready to take over the show for you—listen for his voice!

MUSIC: *"Stars and Stripes Forever."*

MR. CASTLE: Here comes our opening attraction, boys and girls, that mammoth and absolutely unsurpassed Parade of Nations.

SOUND: *Marching feet.*

MR. CASTLE: Look—look at Paul Revere; he's leading the grand parade—riding his beautiful prancing horse, just as he did on that famous ride in 1775—and next—yes, next, rides the Herdboy of Hungary—what strange clothes he wears—what a wild and shaggy mount he rides. Then look! Don Quixote on his faithful old horse—they're followed by a crowd of others—there's every nation—each country represented, Kak, the Copper Eskimo, Heidi, the little Swiss girl, William Tell of Switzerland—every last one of your friends is here. But wait, Pinocchio is jumping into the ring. Believe me, he's not his usual laughing self. What's the news, Pinocchio? Any trace of Toby yet?

PINOCCHIO: Not a sign—Bill Cody traced him as far as Paul Bunyan's dressing room.

MR. CASTLE: Paul Bunyan, the giant? His dressing room is large enough to hide an army.

PINOCCHIO: That's right; but Paul wasn't around, and Bill Cody says there wasn't a sign of Toby any place.

MR. CASTLE: We need action and action right away. Get every member of the circus cast who can be spared to report to me. The Parade of Nations must go on for a few minutes without me.

PINOCCHIO: Emil and the Detectives could help.

MR. CASTLE: A swell idea—now who else?

PINOCCHIO: Winnie-the-Pooh?

MR. CASTLE: Another good idea. Winnie could always find anything he searched for. Get Robin Hood and his Merry Men. Call King Arthur and his Knights. We mustn't miss a single chance to get Little Dog Toby back. He's everyone's favorite.

PINOCCHIO: I'll get them all together. Hepatica, the tall girl, and Paul Bunyan can help too—they'll be able to see in the high places we might miss.

MR. CASTLE: Go to it, Pinocchio—it's back to the show for me. And boys and girls, my humblest apology for this unusual interruption. And listen—here come the Indians! ! !

SOUND: *Indian calls, war whoops. Gradual fading out.*

MR. CASTLE: Ah, here's the searching party now—hello everybody!

CHORUS: Hello, Mr. Castle—

MR. CASTLE: We'll have to get our plans together to find Toby. Who has an idea? How about you, Robin Hood?

ROBIN HOOD: My merry men and I will cover the whole country, but we may need some help. Will you join up, King Arthur?

KING ARTHUR: Indeed sir, in my day, I fought many a battle, rode many a weary mile. Robin Hood, let's be on our way. Pinocchio, you tell the rest what to do.

PINOCCHIO: Hepatica, you'll help us, too—won't you?

HEPATICA: Certainly, for Toby was a great friend of mine in the circus. I'm taking Paul Bunyan with me. Ready, Paul?

PAUL BUNYAN: Ready and able, Miss Hepatica. How about Alice in Wonderland coming with us? Here she is now.

ALICE: Yes, Paul, I'm going along; and Snow-White and the Seven Dwarfs will meet us outside the big tent. But Mr. Castle—do get the rest on their way—we mustn't lose any time.

MR. CASTLE: Alice, you're right. On your way, all of you. You, Katrinka, take Emil and the Detectives with you. Mary Poppins, Caddie Woodlawn, you both go too— and all Toby's animal friends; Ferdinand the Bull, Red Howling Monkey, and the Arkansas Bear. Scout every nook and corner. You, Winnie-the-Pooh, wait a minute, I want to talk to you alone. The rest of you can report back, as soon as you have some news.

CHORUS: So long. Good-by, Mr. Castle—we'll be seeing you—good-by, sir.

MR. CASTLE: Now, Winnie, I'm depending on you.

WINNIE-THE-POOH: You can well do that, Mr. Castle.

MR. CASTLE: All right, Winnie, then off with you, too. Remember that they've traced Toby as far as Paul Bunyan's dressing room. Hunt around, and good luck to you.

WINNIE-THE-POOH: I usually find what I'm after.

MR. CASTLE: [*Laughs*] Especially when it's honey. But don't fail us now, Winnie. Good luck!

WINNIE-THE-POOH: Good-by, sir. I'll find Toby.

MR. CASTLE: Well, it's back to the show for me. I'm awfully late.

MUSIC: *Up and out.*

MR. CASTLE: Late! I'll say I'm late. The Wild West Show has already started.

SOUND: *Cowboy yells, incidental music, etc.*

MR. CASTLE: Boys and girls, another apology, Little Dog Toby is still missing and I know the animal acts were not the same without his performance. But we'll hear results in a few minutes, I know.

SOUND: *Noise of Wild West Show.*

MR. CASTLE: Listen to the noise of the Wild West Show! Hi, there, Bill Cody!

BILL CODY: Hello!—any news of Little Dog Toby yet?

MR. CASTLE: Not yet; still hoping, though. And boys and girls—there's the Lone Ranger—Hello, cowboy!

LONE RANGER: Hi, ho, Sil—ver!

MR. CASTLE: Look at this sight—simply takes your breath away! And the supreme thrill of the show—there goes Toby Tyler taking his horse over the six-bar hurdles. Toby Tyler—the most reckless rider of raring, jumping horses in the whole big-top world.

101

SOUND: *Commotion is heard through Wild West noise. Dog barks violently.*

MR. CASTLE: Folks, it sounds as though the scouting party is back. Yes, listen to that dog bark. I think—in fact —I'm sure they've found Little Dog Toby. How's that for really fast work?

CHORUS: [*Excitedly*] Hi there! Hello—we found him!

MR. CASTLE: Swell, that's great! And Toby doesn't look any the worse for his adventure. Where did you find him, Pinocchio?

PINOCCHIO: I didn't find him, Winnie-the-Pooh did.

MR. CASTLE: Winnie. I should have known. Tell me about it, Winnie!

WINNIE-THE-POOH: [*Ashamed*] Well, Mr. Castle, it was sort of an accident.

MR. CASTLE: Accident? What do you mean?

WINNIE-THE-POOH: Well, you told me they'd traced Toby to Paul's dressing room, so I went there first.

MR. CASTLE: Yes, yes, go on.

WINNIE-THE-POOH: And when I got there I smelled honey. Mr. Bunyan was having pancakes to eat. You know how big his pancakes are.

MR. CASTLE: Six feet in diameter, if they're an inch.

WINNIE-THE-POOH: Yes, sir, and they were all covered with honey—

MR. CASTLE: [*Laughs*] Well—and so?

WINNIE-THE-POOH: So I climbed up on the table and looked at them—just looked.

CHORUS: Of course—just to look at them.

Mr. Castle: Well, but what about Toby?

Winnie-the-Pooh: [*Triumphantly*] There he was asleep. Sound asleep! Covered up from ear to the tip of his tail with one of Paul Bunyan's pancakes—as snug as you please.

Chorus: [*Laugh heartily*]

Mr. Castle: Thanks to Winnie and his love for honey, we've got Little Dog Toby back. Three cheers for Winnie-the-Pooh.

Chorus: Yes, sir—see you later—

Mr. Castle: Before closing the show, boys and girls, we're happy to say that Toby's back—and will be back for every future performance. We hope that you've enjoyed the show—we've done our best to make you happy. Now the barker will show you boys and girls the way out! Here he is now!

Barker: This way out, boys and girls. Careful, young man. Don't tease the animals—this way out! Remember—all your A.O.B.W. favorites are waiting to step out of the covers of your Public Library books to meet you—to thrill you—entertain you—to make you happy. It's just a step to your nearest Branch Library—just a step—and like the great A.O.B.W. Circus—it's *all free* no ticket needed except your Library card. If you haven't a card, get it now and join up with the greatest show on earth.

Jim: Oh! I guess I must have fallen asleep; but gee, that dream about the circus was sure real! I'll go down to the library tomorrow and get some of those books I dreamed about.

A School Library Book Week Play

Adapted for the radio by Manorma Stoecker and Katherine Watson. (Grades 5-6)   10 minutes

CAST OF CHARACTERS

LOUISE

MOTHER

LITTLE LAME PRINCE .... a book character

HEIDI .... a book character

MR. POPPER .... a book character

MRS. POPPER .... a book character

JANIE .... a book character

MRS. BANKS .... a book character

MARY POPPINS .... a book character

BEN .... a book character

TOM .... a book character

KATRINKA .... a book character

SOUNDS

Flying through air   Walking
Noise of penguins   Music
Running

A School Library Book Week Play

LOUISE: Ah, Mother! here it is Book Week and I have to lie in bed with the mumps. All the other children are going to school and I have no one to play with.

MOTHER: Yes, I know, dear, but the doctor said you must be quiet.

LOUISE: What can I do? I am so lonely and tired of being here.

MOTHER: You just try to go to sleep, while I prepare some lunch. I'll wake you when it's ready.

SOUND: *Footsteps fading out.*

LOUISE: [*Yawns*] I am so sick and tired of being in bed all the time. I wish I could suddenly find myself in a place like Wonderland, with all kinds of strange people.

LITTLE LAME PRINCE: Excuse me! Don't be afraid! I'm only a book character. You can call me the Little Lame Prince!

LOUISE: Did I hear someone? Did you say your name was the Little Lame Prince?

LITTLE LAME PRINCE: Yes, and I have come on my magic cloak to take you for a ride.

LOUISE: Where are we going?

LITTLE LAME PRINCE: To the School Library where you can meet some of my friends from Bookland.

SOUND: *Sounds of flying through the air.*

LOUISE: Ah! what fun. Whee! Whee!

LITTLE LAME PRINCE: Here we are and here comes Heidi.

HEIDI: Hello there, what's your name?

LOUISE: My name is Louise. I have never heard of you before. Do you live here?

HEIDI: Yes, I am in the fiction group. I'd like to have you know my Grandfather, and Peter, who tends the sheep high up in the Swiss mountains. There is another book you might like to know about, called *Thimble Summer*. It is about Garnet and all her exciting adventures in Wisconsin long, long ago. Look! here come the penguins and Mr. and Mrs. Popper with their two children, Janie and Billie. Hello, Mrs. Popper.

MRS. POPPER: Hello! Heidi. My, it's good to see you again. Where have you been keeping yourself?

HEIDI: Right here, but I have been visiting many of my friends and they've been so good to me. They never turn my pages down or read with dirty hands, and have recommended me to many of their friends.

MRS. POPPER: We have been busy too. But who is your friend, Heidi? Is she from a new book?

HEIDI: Gracious, I am ashamed of myself for not having introduced you. Mr. and Mrs. Popper and family, this is Louise, a little girl who enjoys books. She is visiting our library and meeting many of my book friends.

LOUISE: I am glad to know you, Mr. and Mrs. Popper. Will you be able to stay for a visit with us?

MRS. POPPER: No! We are on our way to give a performance.

LOUISE: Performance? What kind?

JANIE: Oh, the penguins do all kinds of stunts. Billie and I help them.

LOUISE: I see. You must have lots of fun working with them. That was clever writing the names on their backs.

JANIE: That was Dad's idea. I'll never forget that day I came home from school and saw Captain Cook strutting around. Let me tell you how we got him.

MR. POPPER: Oh! no you don't, Janie; that's my story.

JANIE: O.K., if you insist—go ahead.

MR. POPPER: All right. Mama was mending socks and I was reading *Antarctic Adventures.* Soon Mama said, "I'm going to bed. Tomorrow is Thursday, September 30th, and I have to go to the first meeting of the Ladies' Aid and Missionary Society." I said, "You mean tonight is Wednesday, September 29th." She said, "Yes, I suppose it is. But what of it?" I hastily put down my book and turned on the radio and heard Admiral Drake's voice from the South Pole saying, "Hello, Mamma; hello, Papa! Hello, Mr. Popper down in Stillwater! This is Admiral Drake broadcasting from the Antarctic. Thanks for the letter and pictures. Watch for an answer, but not by letter. Signing off— signing off."

MR. POPPER: Were we excited? We could hardly wait to see the surprise. Finally, in a few days it came—a real live penguin! And we named him Captain Cook.

MR. POPPER: Well, we'll have to be running along now; we mustn't be late for our performance. We're glad to have met you, Louise.

LOUISE: I'm glad to have met you, too; and I'll be anxious to read about you. Good-by.

MRS. POPPER: Good-by, and come and see us soon.

SOUND: *Noise of penguins.*

LOUISE: This is a new experience for me, Heidi. I am wondering if you could tell me about some good boys' books. I'd like to meet Tom Sawyer.

HEIDI: Of course you can meet Tom. Let's hurry or we will miss him. He's probably out playing with the gang. Come on, Louise.

SOUND: *Running.*

LOUISE: There's Tom whitewashing the fence now. Let's listen in!

BEN: [*Fading in*] Say, Tom, let me whitewash a little.

TOM: No, no. I reckon it wouldn't hardly do, Ben. You see, Aunt Polly's awful particular about this fence right here on the street. You know, if it was the back fence I wouldn't mind, and she wouldn't. Yes, she's awful particular about this fence. I reckon there ain't one boy in a thousand, maybe two thousand, that can do it the way it's got to be done.

BEN: No! Is that so? Oh! come now, lemme just try! Only just a little. If you was me, I'd let you, Tom.

TOM: Ben, I'd like to, honest Injun; but Aunt Polly—well, Jim wanted to do it, but she wouldn't let him; Sid wanted to do it, and she wouldn't let Sid. Now don't you see how I'm fixed? If you was to tackle this fence and anything was to happen to it—

BEN: Ah, shucks! I'll be just as careful. Say, I'll give you the core of my apple.

TOM: Well, here. No, Ben, don't. I'm afeared.

BEN: I'll give you all of it. Come on!

TOM: All right, Ben; but be careful.

MUSIC: *Bridge.*

HEIDI: Tom was a great boy; and you know, when the middle of the afternoon came, he was literally rolling in wealth. Not only had he plenty of company, but the fence had three coats of whitewash on it. And now, Louise, I'll take you to one of the prettiest lanes in Book-land. It is Cherry-Tree Lane.

LOUISE: Oh, goody, let's go.

SOUND: *Walking.*

HEIDI: This is called Cherry-Tree Lane. The smallest house in this block is where Mr. and Mrs. Banks live with Michael, Jane, and the twins. Wouldn't you like to pay them a short visit?

LOUISE: Yes, but it looks like they have company.

HEIDI: I believe they have. Mrs. Banks is interviewing Mary Poppins. She is trying to find a new nurse for her children. Let's just listen in for a few minutes.

MRS. BANKS: You'll find they are nice children, and they are no trouble at all. Now, what about references, Mary Poppins?

MARY POPPINS: I make it a rule never to give references. I find it a very old-fashioned idea.

MRS. BANKS: Very well, then, we won't bother about them. I only asked, of course, in case—well, never mind.

MARY POPPINS: Now, I'd like to meet these nice children.

MRS. BANKS: The nursery is upstairs. This way.

LOUISE: What an odd-looking person. She looks just like a scarecrow. Look at her gracefully sliding up the bannister!

HEIDI: There's something strange and extraordinary about Mary Poppins—something that's frightening and at the same time fascinating. Oh, here comes someone you should meet. Katrinka is from Russia.

109

LOUISE: Hello, Katrinka. Tell us something about Russia, will you?

KATRINKA: In Russia it is so very cold in winter that the peasants or poor folks have to sleep on the top of the oven to keep warm at night. Peter and I always slept on our oven; but we were more fortunate than the others, for we had plenty to eat and a comfortable home. Father and Mother could read and write. Because Father had a printing press, he and Mother were sent to Siberia and Peter and I were left alone.

LOUISE: Oh, weren't you afraid without parents?

KATRINKA: I didn't have time to be afraid. I took care of Peter and then we went to St. Petersburg. With the aid of Madame Morenski, I was able to enter the Russian Ballet; and finally I danced for the Czar of Russia.

MUSIC: *Musical curtain.*

MOTHER: Louise, Louise! Wake up. Here's your lunch.

LOUISE: [*Waking and yawning*] Oh—a—aoh! Where am I?

MOTHER: Wake up! You must have gone to sleep.

LOUISE: Oh! I've just had such a wonderful dream. I'd like to know more about these book-people I've been dreaming about.

MOTHER: I'm going downtown this afternoon; I'll stop at the Public Library and have the children's librarian pick out some good books for you.

Fairy Tales

Bremen Town Musicians

From *Grimm's Fairy Tales,* by Jakob and Wilhelm Grimm.
Adapted for radio by Toni Hult.   (Grades 4-5)   15 minutes

CAST OF CHARACTERS

DONKEY
DOG
CAT
ROOSTER
1ST ROBBER
2ND ROBBER
3RD ROBBER
4TH ROBBER
CHIEF OF ROBBERS

SOUNDS

Footsteps
Weeping
Dog barking and pant-
ing
Cat meowing
Rooster crowing
Snoring
Shuffling

Window crashing
Running feet
Cat spitting and scratching
Tearing sound
Donkey kicking
Flutter of wings
Music

Bremen Town Musicians

MUSIC: *Introduction and under.*

ANNOUNCER: Good afternoon, boys and girls. Today we take you to the land of make-believe in a radio play, the Bremen Town Musicians. This story takes place in the days when donkeys, dogs, cats, and roosters could talk to each other just as you boys and girls do. You don't believe it? Well, listen! It's the donkey speaking—he's talking to himself, and he seems to be in trouble, too—

MUSIC: *Out.*

DONKEY: Something's up—I know there is. That master of mine, he means to kill me, just because I'm old and lame and can no longer carry the heavy loads I once did. Well, I'm getting out of here while the getting's good. Oh, ho, here's the path to Bremen.

SOUND: *Walking.*

DONKEY: Guess I'll run away and never come back. From now on, I've got to make my own living. But how? I might join up with a band of street musicians; I really have a lovely singing voice. But it's lonesome walking by myself. Wish I had some company.

SOUND: *Weeping.*

DONKEY: Oh, I hear someone crying.

SOUND: *Walking out. Dog barks dolefully. Panting.*

114

DONKEY: [*Whispers*] Well, well, a big hunting dog, crying his eyes out. [*Aloud*] Hey, friend Dog, why are you panting so hard? [*Clucks sympathetically through next speech*]

DOG: Oh, Oh! Something terrible's going to happen to me. For years I've been most faithful to my master. I've guarded his house night and day, and gone on all his hunting trips with him. Now that I'm old, half blind and deaf, my master means to kill me and sell my hide. Now that I'm too old to earn my living, I will surely starve by the wayside.

DONKEY: Good friend, my case is much the same as yours! But I'm not wasting my time crying. Know what I'm going to do? I'm on my way to Bremen-Town and there I plan to become a musician.

DOG: A musician!

DONKEY: Sure. Why don't you come, too?

DOG: Now that is an idea! For I, too , have a lovely voice.

SOUND: *Walking.*

DONKEY: Come on. On our way then. I will play the lute and you can sound the kettle-drum—that will make fine music. And the people will be sure to throw us a few pennies—maybe other things, too.

DOG: You're right! We'll be a big success!

SOUND: *Cat meowing dismally.*

DOG: [*Whispers*] Listen, brother Donkey. Someone's in trouble. Why, it's a cat!

DONKEY: [*Whispers*] Yah, and he's got a face as long as a three days' drizzle. [*Aloud*] Hey, old whiskers, what's wrong with you?

115

CAT: [*Meow*] I'm running away—from home.

DOG: Yah, so we see—

CAT: My life is at stake, for I'm too old to work. For years I've kept my master's house free from rats and mice. Now my eyes are dull and my teeth are blunt. All I ask is to sit by the fireside and dream of my past glories. But because I can no longer work, my mistress wants to get rid of me. Just this morning she tried to drown me. So I ran away.

DONKEY and DOG: We don't blame you. A dirty shame!

CAT: But where can I go, and what can I do?

DONKEY: Never say die, old Cat. Why don't you join us?

CAT: Thanks. But how can I make a living?

SOUND: *Walking.*

DONKEY: We're on our way to Bremen-Town to become musicians. Say, old Cat, you've had a lot of practice serenading. Why, you'd fit right into our band.

CAT: Yes, I have a lovely voice, I admit. People have liked my serenading, so much so, they'd get up in the middle of the night to throw things at me, just to attract my attention.

DOG: Hurry up. We have a long way to go.

SOUND: *Rooster crows dismally. Cock-a-doodle-doo. Walking out.*

CAT: Listen to that ragged old rooster there on the farmyard gate.

DONKEY: Hey, Rooster, you seem to be in a dismal mood. What's up?

ROOSTER: You'd crow dismally, too, if your mistress planned to throw you into a pot and cook you for her Sunday dinner.

DONKEY, CAT and DOG: [*Whistles*] Oh, my goodness! Horrible, old Rooster, horrible!

ROOSTER: Cock-a-doodle-doo. Since I shall lose my head tonight—cock-a-doodle-doo. I thought I'd crow as long —cock-a-doodle-doo—as my head was on my shoulders. Cock-a-doodle-doo.

DONKEY: Hold on, friend Rooster. No need to let yourself be killed!

ROOSTER: That's what you think, brother Donkey.

DONKEY: Join us, friend Rooster, why don't you? We're off to Bremen-Town to become musicians.

SOUND: *Walking.*

ROOSTER: Gee, brother Donkey, I'd like that! Cock-a-doodle-doo.

DONKEY: [*Admiringly*] You do have, friend Rooster, a fine lusty voice, I must say. While we're all making music together, you could put in a cock-a-doodle-doo here and there.

CAT: Let's move along a little faster. We want to get to Bremen before dark.

ANNOUNCER: But the town of Bremen couldn't be reached in a day. All day they kept walking; and when darkness came, the four weary travelers found themselves in the middle of a forest, where they decided to spend the night. The dog and donkey lay down under a huge tree to sleep.

SOUND: *Snoring.*

117

ANNOUNCER: The cat climbed up and made himself comfortable on a big lower branch, but the rooster flew up to the top-most tip of the tree where he could have a bird's eye view of the entire country-side.

ROOSTER: Hey, friends. There's a house nearby. I see a light.

DONKEY: Huh! What's that? What did you say?

CAT: You see a house!

DOG: Oh, I bet they'd be glad to see us. Let's move on.

SOUND: *Walking.*

DONKEY: Undoubtedly. Undoubtedly. Let's be on our way. These quarters are none too comfortable. I miss the barnyard.

DOG: I could use a good bone with a little meat on it, too.

CAT: Oh, for a saucerful of good sweet milk.

ROOSTER: And for me some juicy scraps from the dinner table.

ANNOUNCER: So the four travelers walked on and on. In the starlight—there wasn't any moon—they could see the house quite clearly now, and the little glimmer of light grew bigger and bigger.

SOUND: *Walking.*

DOG: There's the door to the little house. Before we knock, we'd better take a peep and see what's going on.

CAT: Donkey, you're the tallest. Creep up to the window and look in.

SOUND: *Tiptoeing.*

118

DONKEY: Friends, you have the best ideas! Sh-h, my, oh, my! My, oh, my!

ROOSTER: What is it, brother Donkey? What do you see?

DONKEY: [*Whispers*] What do I see? A table stacked with food and drink!

SOUND: *All whistle softly but happily.*

DONKEY: And a band of robbers! Sitting around the table! Gobbling up the food!

ALL: *Whistle in consternation.*

CAT: What'll we do?

ROOSTER: How'll we get rid of them?

DOG: We must think up a plan.

SOUND: *Shuffling and soft grunts.*

DONKEY: Shh! I have it. We'll serenade 'em. They'll like it so well they'll invite us in. Now very quietly I'll raise my fore feet up to the ledge of the window. Shh! Dog, you, jump up on my back. That's the idea. Sh! Sh! and, old Cat, you climb up on Dog's back. That's right, Rooster, right on the cat's shoulder.

ROOSTER: All set, brother Donkey.

DONKEY: Oh, I wish I'd brought my baton. Well, I'll just tap my hoof.

SOUND: *Four taps to the count.*

DONKEY: Softly; one-two-three-four—begin.

ALL: *Make music.*

SOUND: *Wild noise. Window crashing. Running.*

ROBBERS: Demons! Witches! Run—run for your lives! To the forest! To the forest!

DONKEY: Well, friends, it's all ours! Those robbers have no appreciation of fine music. They ran off, leaving the whole feast to us.

ANNOUNCER: And so the four famished travelers took possession of the robbers' den. And how they did eat! They ate until they couldn't eat any more. They decided to go to bed without even stacking the dishes, for they were very tired after their hard day's travel. Carefully they blew out the light. The donkey went outside to the barnyard and lay down on a hay stack. The dog stretched himself under the table where he might guard the door. The cat sat on the hearth beside the warm ashes and shampooed her coat. And the rooster found a fine place to perch on the gable of the house. Meanwhile, out in the forest, the robbers decided that perhaps they'd allowed themselves to become unduly frightened and they came out to take another look. All was quiet. No light in their den. All seemed safe and well. Therefore, the chief of the robbers ordered one of the boldest of his gang to return, steal into the den, light the lamp, and look around. The bold robber did as he was told.

SOUND: *Tiptoeing.*

ANNOUNCER: Finding everything quiet, he tiptoed into the kitchen to light a lamp. In the darkness the cat's eyes glowed by the hearth. The robber mistook them for the smoldering embers of the fireplace, and tried to light his match. Then in the dark the old cat went into action.

SOUND: *Spitting and scratching.*

1ST ROBBER: Hey! What's that? Why, the coals in the fireplace are alive. Oh, where's the kitchen door? I can't see! It's so dark! Help! Help! Help!

SOUND: *Dog barks and makes tearing sound. Running.*

1ST ROBBER: Oh, some devil, hiding under the table, bit me on the leg. Thank goodness, I got out of that den alive. I'll run out through the barnyard and hide behind the hay stack.

SOUND: *Donkey brays and kicks.*

1ST ROBBER: Oh, there's another demon here. It hit me with a club. Oh, my chest! I can't breathe! I'll have to go back past the den, the way I came.

SOUND: *Tiptoeing. Panting. Flutter of wings.*

ROOSTER: [*Spitefully*] Cock-a-doodle-doo. Cock-a-doodle-doo.

1ST ROBBER: Horrors! An old witch flew down and almost pecked my eyes out. [*Fighting*] Get away! Get away! Shoo! Oh, at last, I'm free!

SOUND: *Running very fast.*

1ST ROBBER: Now I'll run back to the forest [*Puff*] just as fast as I can! [*Puff*] Those wicked demons [*Puff*]; they almost killed me. [*Puff*] Hey, gang, I'm back. And I'll never go back there as long as I live.

2ND ROBBER: What happened?

3RD ROBBER: Tell us!

4TH ROBBER: What was that awful racket?

2ND ROBBER: Why, you're all bloody!

1ST ROBBER: Our den's haunted!

ALL: Haunted!

121

1st Robber: Witches and demons and ghosts!

2nd Robber: Yes, yes!

3rd Robber: Go on; tell us about it!

4th Robber: Go on!

1st Robber: In the house [*Puff*] by the hearth [*Puff*] sits the most horrible witch. [*Puff*] When I went to light my match [*Puff*] she breathed her hot breath on me and scratched my face with her long finger nails.

2nd Robber: Oh, your face. Terrible wounds. [*Clucks sympathetically*]

Chief: That witch is worse than a cat.

1st Robber: Under the table lies a dangerous man [*Puff*] with a butcher knife. [*Puff*] He slashed out [*Puff*] and stabbed me in the leg as I rushed out through the door.

Chief: A wicked cut, if I ever saw one. That demon's a dirty dog!

1st Robber: Then I thought I'd make my get-away through the barnyard. As I ran past the hay stack, a black monster gave me a whack with a club.

2nd Robber: My goodness!

3rd Robber: Terrible!

4th Robber: Horrible!

1st Robber: Why, that demon must've had a club like the hoof of a donkey. There upon the roof, where no human could possibly climb, sat a judge, who cried, "Bring that rogue here!" So I hurried away as fast as I could.

Announcer: After this the robbers never dared go back to the house, and the four Bremen town musicians found themselves so well off where they were, that there they stayed.

Cinderella

From *Grimm's Fairy Tales,* by Jakob and Wilhelm Grimm.
Adapted for radio by Katherine Watson.   (Grades 3-4)   10 minutes

CAST OF CHARACTERS

CINDERELLA
STEPMOTHER
1ST STEPSISTER
2ND STEPSISTER
FAIRY GODMOTHER
PRINCE
HERALD

SOUNDS

Music
Footsteps running
Swishing sound
Clock striking twelve.

Knocking at door
Trumpet
Door opening

Cinderella

ANNOUNCER: This is the story of Cinderella, who is sitting sadly before the fire, shabbily dressed. Her stepmother and stepsisters are talking over plans for the ball. We hear Cinderella talking softly to herself.

CINDERELLA: I am so sad. Why did my father marry again after my mother died. Now I am just a kitchen drudge and have to do all the hard, dirty tasks. My stepmother and my stepsisters hate me. [*Aloud to stepmother*] How I wish I were going to the ball tonight! Oh, please take me with you.

STEPMOTHER: You! What would an ugly thing like you do going to a ball? You will stay home and see that the fire doesn't go out. Go now, and help your sisters dress.

1ST STEPSISTER: Come here quickly, Cinderella, and arrange my hair. I shall wear my dress of purple satin with a long train, and my diamond necklace.

2ND STEPSISTER: Come here at once, Cinderella, and fasten my dress. I shall wear my lovely blue velvet with trimmings of gold lace. I hope the Prince will dance with me.

1ST STEPSISTER: Come along, sister; it's time to go to the ball.

MUSIC: *Bridge.*

CINDERELLA: How I wish I could go to the ball tonight! I've heard that the Prince is going to be there. If I only had a beautiful dress! Oh, dear! Oh, dear!

124

SOUND: *Knocking at door. Supernatural sound effects and door opening.*

FAIRY GODMOTHER: Why are you crying so hard, my dear?

CINDERELLA: Who are you?

FAIRY GODMOTHER: I'm your fairy godmother.

CINDERELLA: My—fairy—godmother!

FAIRY GODMOTHER: You want to go to the ball, is that it? Well, perhaps we can find a way. Have you a large pumpkin?

CINDERELLA: Oh, we have plenty of pumpkins. This is a nice one.

FAIRY GODMOTHER: Take it outside the door and put it down. Now I will repeat a charm and see what happens. Wany, Wany, Wandu Wam. Fairy powers hither come.

SOUND: *Transformation sound.*

CINDERELLA: Oh, fairy Godmother, the pumpkin has turned into a beautiful gold coach. But where are the horses?

FAIRY GODMOTHER: Bring me the mouse trap, Cinderella.

CINDERELLA: Here it is. Look, Godmother! Here are six fat mice, all alive.

FAIRY GODMOTHER: Lift the door a little and now see what has happened.

CINDERELLA: Oh, the brown mice have changed into six beautiful horses, with long tails. Why their harness is shining with silver. Now we need someone to drive the coach.

FAIRY GODMOTHER: So we do! Let me see. What shall we do for a driver?

CINDERELLA: How would a rat do, Godmother? I saw a large gray one in the trap a little while ago.

FAIRY GODMOTHER: The very thing, my child. We'll make a fine coachman of him. Put him out with the coach and the horses. Now find the six lizards behind the watering pot. Bring them to me!

CINDERELLA: Yes, Godmother.

SOUND: *Footsteps.*

CINDERELLA: Here they are—here they are.

FAIRY GODMOTHER: Now I'm going to repeat the charm again. Wany, Wany, Wando Wam. Fairy powers hither come.

CINDERELLA: Oh, footmen!

FAIRY GODMOTHER: Yes, there are your footmen. Now you can go to the ball.

CINDERELLA: But Godmother, not in these rags!

FAIRY GODMOTHER: Yes, you do need a pretty dress for the ball. I'll wave this fairy wand and change your torn garments into a gown of silver and gold.

CINDERELLA: Oh! How beautiful! I never had a dress like this. How can I ever thank you, Godmother?

FAIRY GODMOTHER: Here are your glass slippers. Have a good time at the ball; but one thing you must remember, my child. My power lasts no longer than twelve o'clock. If you stay one minute later than that, you will lose everything my magic power has given you. Your carriage will be a big yellow pumpkin, your horses scampering mice, your footmen lizards, and you will be wearing rags again.

CINDERELLA: I promise, dear Godmother, to leave before twelve.

FAIRY GODMOTHER: Then come, Princess Cinderella, your gold coach is waiting.

MUSIC: *Musical curtain.*

ANNOUNCER: We now see a ballroom, brilliantly lighted. Waltz music is heard in the background. Cinderella enters, and she is led to the Prince.

MUSIC: *Waltz music fading in.*

PRINCE: Welcome to my palace, lovely Princess.

CINDERELLA: Thank you, Your Highness.

PRINCE: May I have you as my partner for this dance?

CINDERELLA: With pleasure.

PRINCE: How beautifully you dance!

MUSIC: *Bridge.*

CINDERELLA: I'm having such a wonderful time. Everyone is so kind, and I love to dance. But, oh, dear! The clock is beginning to strike twelve.

SOUND: *Clock striking twelve—one, two, three, four, five, six, seven, eight, nine—*

PRINCE: But surely you don't have to go so soon. The ball will last for hours.

CINDERELLA: I'm very sorry, but I must go.

SOUND: *Clock still striking—ten, eleven, twelve. Then footsteps running.*

PRINCE: Oh, she has gone in such a hurry that she has left one of her dainty slippers behind. I would give anything in the world to know who she is.

MUSIC: *Musical curtain.*

ANNOUNCER: It is now the next day. We find the step-mother and her two daughters talking over the ball of the night before.

1ST STEPSISTER: There was the loveliest princess at the ball.

2ND STEPSISTER: She wore the most beautiful dress and jewels. And she wore glass slippers that sparkled as she danced.

CINDERELLA: How I wish I could have seen her!

SOUND: *Trumpet.*

1ST STEPSISTER: Why, what can that be?

STEPMOTHER: It is a magnificent herald. He is reading a proclamation to the people and the Prince is with him.

HERALD: Hear ye, hear ye! The son of the King makes public that he will marry the maiden whose foot will exactly fit this slipper.

STEPMOTHER: My dear girls, what a chance for you! If one of you can put on the slipper, you will become the Princess.

2ND STEPSISTER: The herald is stopping before our door. Quick, quick! Look your best.

1ST STEPSISTER: Quick, they are coming in.

HERALD: Hear ye, hear ye! Who wishes to try on the slipper? At the ball last night there was a most beautiful princess. The Prince was charmed with her and begged her to stay until the ball was over, but at twelve o'clock she ran away. She lost this slipper and the Prince has ordered it to be tried on the foot of every lady in the kingdom.

1ST STEPSISTER: Oh, I'm sure it will fit me, easily. O-u-c-h. Oh, dear; I can't get it on; it hurts my heel.

2ND STEPSISTER: Then let me try. O-u-c-h. It's no use; it squeezes my toes.

HERALD: Are there no others in this house whom the slipper would be likely to fit? I thought I saw another, as I passed the window.

STEPMOTHER: That must have been our scullion maid.

HERALD: But I must let her try on the slipper. I have orders to fit it on the foot of every maiden in the kingdom. Sit down, beautiful maiden, and try on this slipper. [*Pause*] Why! It fits like wax.

ALL: Oh! Oh! Oh!

SOUND: *Tranformation sound.*

GODMOTHER: Cinderella, take the other slipper from your pocket, and slip it on your foot. I will now touch you with my magic wand and all your splendor will return.

HERALD: Make way for the Prince!

SOUND: *Footsteps.*

PRINCE: My beautiful Princess! You are more lovely than ever. Come with me to my palace where we will live happily ever after.

Hansel and Grethel

From *Grimm's Fairy Tales,* by Jakob and Wilhelm Grimm.
Adapted for radio by Katherine Watson. (Grades 3, 4-5)   10 minutes

CAST OF CHARACTERS

HANSEL .... son of the woodcutter
GRETHEL .... daughter of the woodcutter
FATHER .... woodcutter
STEPMOTHER
WITCH

SOUNDS

Music   Oven door banging
Footsteps   Duck swimming
Knock   Running
Door opening   Rattle of dishes
Door closing   Key in lock

Hansel and Grethel

ANNOUNCER: Once upon a time there lived on the outskirts of a large forest a poor woodcutter with his wife and his two children; the boy was called Hansel and the girl Grethel. Once there was a great famine in the land, and the father couldn't even provide them with daily bread. As he lay one night thinking of this, he sighed heavily, and said to his wife—

FATHER: What's to become of us? How are we to feed our poor children, when we no longer have anything even for ourselves?

STEPMOTHER: I'll tell you what, Husband, early tomorrow morning we'll take the children out into the thickest part of the woods. We will then light a fire and give them a piece of bread; then we will go to our work and leave them alone. They won't be able to find their way home, and we shall be rid of them.

FATHER: No, Wife. I won't do that. I cannot find it in my heart to leave my children alone in the forest. The wild animals would soon come and tear them to pieces.

STEPMOTHER: Then we must all four die of hunger.

FATHER: But I can't help feeling sorry for the poor children.

ANNOUNCER: The two children had not been able to sleep for hunger. They had heard what their stepmother had said to their father. Grethel began weeping bitterly and said to Hansel—

GRETHEL: It is all over with us now, Hansel.

HANSEL: Be quiet, Grethel. Do not be troubled. I have an idea that will help us find the way home. I'll get some white pebbles from the front of the house and drop them on the path. Be at ease, dear little sister, and sleep in peace. God will not forsake us.

MUSIC: *Musical curtain.*

STEPMOTHER: Get up, Hansel and Grethel, you lie-abeds; we're all going to the forest to fetch wood. Here is a piece of bread for each of you children. This is for your dinner; and you must not eat it before then, because you will get nothing else.

ANNOUNCER: Grethel put the bread under her apron because Hansel had the pebbles in his pocket. Then they all set out together on the way to the forest. Hansel dropped the white pebbles one after another along the road. We now hear the father say—

FATHER: Now, children, pile up some wood and I will light a fire so you will not feel the cold. Lie down by the fire and rest yourselves; we are going into the forest to cut wood. When we have finished, we will come back for you.

SOUND: *Footsteps.*

MUSIC: *Musical curtain.*

GRETHEL: Oh! how long we have been here! Why don't our parents come back? How shall we ever get out of this wood?

HANSEL: Wait a bit, till the moon is up, and then we can easily find the way home. See, it is getting light. I think we can find our way by following the pebbles.

SOUND: *Footsteps.*

MUSIC: *Bridge.*

GRETHEL: We have walked all through the night, but there is our house at last! I'll knock.

SOUND: *Knocking at door. Footsteps approaching. Door opening.*

STEPMOTHER: You naughty children, why did you sleep so long in the wood? We thought you were never coming home. You'll have to go without your supper.

MUSIC: *Musical curtain.*

HANSEL: [*Whispering*] Oh! do you hear what our mother is saying? She says that everything is eaten up once more; there is only half a loaf of bread in the house, so they must get rid of us.

GRETHEL: Oh, dear! Oh, dear!

HANSEL: Do not cry, Grethel; go to sleep quietly. The good Lord will help us.

ANNOUNCER: Early the next morning, the stepmother came and pulled the children out of bed. She gave them each a piece of bread—smaller than before. On the way to the wood, Hansel crumbled the bread that he had in his pocket and threw the crumbs on their path. They have now come into the deep forest and we hear the stepmother say—

STEPMOTHER: Just sit here, you children, and when you are tired you can sleep a little. We are going into the forest to cut wood. In the evening when we are ready to go home, we will come and get you.

MUSIC: *Musical curtain.*

GRETHEL: You take some of my bread, Hansel, because you have scattered yours by the way. I wonder what has happened to our parents.

HANSEL: Just wait, Grethel, until the moon comes up, and then we shall be able to see our way home by the crumbs of bread that I have left along the path. Oh! Oh! Grethel, the birds must have picked them all up. I can't find them. I'm so very tired.

MUSIC: *Musical curtain.*

HANSEL: Why, we've walked for three days. I'm hungry, too; for all we've had are the few berries that we've found on the ground. Oh, look! what is that?

GRETHEL: Why, Hansel, it looks like a little house.

HANSEL: And it's all made out of gingerbread.

GRETHEL: It has windows of clear sugar.

HANSEL: And see the gable of raisins.

GRETHEL: What is the fence made of?

HANSEL: It's just like a ginger cookie fence.

GRETHEL: I will eat a bit of the roof; you, Hansel, can eat some of the window—that will taste sweet. Why, I hear someone in the house.

WITCH: Nibble, nibble, gnaw
Who is nibbling at my little house?

CHILDREN: The wind, the wind.
The wind from heaven.

SOUND: *Door opening.*

HANSEL: Oh! I'm so frightened. She looks like a witch.

WITCH: Oh, ho! you dear children; who led you here? Just come in and stay with me. No harm shall befall you.

SOUND: *Door closing.*

WITCH: You must be hungry. Here is some milk, and pancakes with sugar, apples, and nuts; and after you've eaten, here are your two little beds.

SOUND: *Rattle of dishes into musical bridge.*

HANSEL: I feel so much better now. I think we must be in heaven, Grethel.

ANNOUNCER: The old woman appeared to be most friendly; but she was really an old witch who had waylaid children, and had only built the little gingerbread house in order to lure them in. When anyone came into her power, she killed, cooked, and ate them. Early in the morning she seized Hansel and carried him into a little stable and barred the door. She then went back to Grethel.

WITCH: Get up, you lazy-bones; fetch water and cook something for your brother. When he's fat, I'll eat him up.

GRETHEL: Oh, dear! Oh, dear!

MUSIC: *Musical curtain.*

SOUND: *Footsteps.*

WITCH: Hansel, put out your finger, that I may feel if you are getting fat.

ANNOUNCER: Hansel, however, held out a little bone; and the old woman, unable to see well because of weak eyes, thought it was his finger and wondered why he grew

135

no fatter. When four weeks had passed and Hansel still remained thin, she lost patience and we hear her say to Grethel—

WITCH: Now then, Grethel, be quick and bring some water. Let Hansel be fat or thin, tomorrow I will kill him and cook him.

GRETHEL: Dear God, do help us! If only the wild beasts in the forest had but eaten us, then at least we could have died together.

WITCH: First we will do the baking. I've heated the oven already, and kneaded the dough. Creep in and see if it is hot enough so that the bread may be baked.

GRETHEL: I don't know how to do it; how do I get in?

WITCH: Stupid goose! The door is large enough. Just look, I can get in myself.

GRETHEL: [*To herself*] Oh, my chance at last. I'll push her in.

SOUND: *Oven door banging.*

GRETHEL: Hurrah! We're free. Now I can let Hansel out.

SOUND: *Key in lock. Door opening.*

GRETHEL: Hurrah, the old witch is dead. I pushed her in the oven.

HANSEL: You are a brave girl, Grethel. How wonderful that we are saved! Let's fill our pockets full of pearls and jewels from these chests.

GRETHEL: Now let's go. I'm anxious to get home.

SOUND: *Footsteps.*

136

MUSIC: *Musical curtain.*

HANSEL: We've been walking such a long way. Here is a lake. How will we ever get across? There isn't a bridge of any kind.

GRETHEL: And there isn't a boat, either. But here comes a white duck. I will ask her if she will help us over.
Duck, duck, here we stand,
Hansel and Grethel on the land.
Stepping-stones and bridge we lack;
Carry us over on your nice white back.

HANSEL: Here she is. Let's both get on her back.

GRETHEL: No, that will be too heavy for the little duck; she shall carry us across separately.

SOUND: *Duck swimming in water.*

MUSIC: *Musical curtain.*

HANSEL: Oh! here we are all safe and sound on the shore. Let's run, for I see our house.

SOUND: *Running feet.*

GRETHEL: Oh! Father, where are you?

FATHER: Here I am, children.

HANSEL: It's so good to be home. But where is our stepmother?

FATHER: She is dead. I haven't known one happy hour since we left you children in the forest.

HANSEL: Open your pinafore, Grethel, and show Father the precious stones we have brought home.

FATHER: Now I am sure we're all going to live happily ever after.

Holidays

The Christmas Monks

A story by Mary E. Wilkins Freeman taken from the book, *Christmas Candles*, compiled by Elsie Hobart Carter. Published by Henry Holt & Company. Reproduced by permission of the publishers. Adapted for radio by Katherine Watson. (Grades 5-6)   30 minutes

CAST OF CHARACTERS

MISTRESS LONGLANE ⎫

⎬ .... from a distant village

DOLLY ⎭

MISTRESS SPINNING .... village mother

ANNETTA ⎫

MARIANNA ⎬ .... village children

PETER ⎭

GILBERT .... carpenter's apprentice

ROBIN .... forester's son

COURTIER

PRINCE

GREGORY ⎫

ANSELM ⎬ .... Brethren of the Monastery

HILARION ⎭

ROSALIA .... Peter's little sister

AMBROSE .... the Leech, one of the Brethren

ABBOT

MONKS

VILLAGERS

SOUNDS

Footsteps   Opening of letter
Thump   Gallop of horses
Street noises   Music
Footsteps running

The Christmas Monks

ANNOUNCER: Our play of the Christmas monks takes place the first week in April, on a country road leading by a monastery. On the wall is a large sign which says, "Wanted, by the Christmas monks, two good boys to assist in garden work. Applicants will be examined by Father Anselm and Father Gregory on April 8th, 9th, and 10th." As the play opens we hear Mistress Longlane, a newly-arrived villager, talking to her daughter—

MISTRESS LONGLANE: Oh! Look at this sign on the monastery wall. Now what may be the meaning of this?

DOLLY: What is it, Mother?

MISTRESS LONGLANE: It says: "Wanted, by the Christmas monks, two good boys to assist in garden work." The Christmas monks? What manner of men are the Christmas monks? Here comes a woman from the village. I'll ask her.

SOUND: *Footsteps.*

MISTRESS LONGLANE: Good morning, Mistress. Have you a moment to spare for a stranger in the country?

MISTRESS SPINNING: Yes, indeed.

MISTRESS LONGLANE: May I ask the meaning of this strange sign that hangs upon the wall?

MISTRESS SPINNING: Oh, you must indeed be a stranger in the land if you have never heard of the Christmas monks. If you have come to make your home in our village, you'll soon learn that this is the home of the Christmas monks, who keep the gardens in which all the Christmas toys are grown.

142

Mistress Longlane: The Christmas toys!

Dolly: Why, I thought Santa Claus brought them all.

Mistress Spinning: So he does, my dear. He takes them to the children, of course, but this is the garden where he comes to load his sleigh. You cannot see inside, but that garden is just full of toys.

Mistress Longlane: You don't say!

Mistress Spinning: Yes, the Christmas monks have a wonderful garden with beds for rocking-horses, beds for dolls, beds for drums, picture-books, skates and balls. And the seeds are just the tiniest bits of dolls, drums and balls, so little that you can hardly see them at all.

Mistress Longlane: What do the monks do?

Mistress Spinning: Why, they plant the seeds, take care of the garden, and see that the toys are all ripe and ready for good old Santa Claus by Christmas time. The Christmas monks are so full of the Christmas spirit that it lasts them all the year round, and they go about putting heart into people who get sad and discouraged. But I think I see some of the children coming for the examination.

Sound: *Street noises. People walking. Noise of children.*

Mistress Longlane: Ah, yes. Is that to take place this afternoon?

Mistress Spinning: Yes, this is the last afternoon. The good Fathers have already held two examinations and, will you believe it? They haven't found two boys who are good enough, though they've examined *hundreds*. Oh! Here come Annetta and Marianna, two girls from the village.

143

SOUND: *Footsteps.*

ANNETTA: Oh, Marianna, don't you wonder whom the good Fathers will choose?

MARIANNA: Yes, indeed I do, Annetta. Why, there aren't very many more boys to examine. Ssh! Here comes Peter with his little sister Rosalia.

SOUND: *Footsteps.*

PETER: See, Rosalia, that's the sign, and the monks come right here to examine the boys.

ROSALIA: Oh, Peter, I wish they'd take you to work in the Christmas garden!

PETER: There isn't much chance of that, I'm afraid. But, come sister, I'd better take you home. You might get hurt in the crowd.

SOUND: *Footsteps.*

ANNETTA: Marianna, why wouldn't Peter try for the examination?

MARIANNA: He's going to try today, I believe. He wouldn't before because he is so modest.

ANNETTA: But he's the very best boy in the village, and so good to his parents and his little lame sister! Oh! Here come Gilbert and Robin, who are going to be examined by the monks.

SOUND: *Footsteps.*

GILBERT: I wish we had been here yesterday, Robin.

ROBIN: Well, perhaps we'll have a better chance today; there aren't so many of us to choose from.

144

MISTRESS LONGLANE: Why, who's this coming down the road?

SOUND: *Confusion on the road.*

MISTRESS SPINNING: Mercy on us, 'tis the Prince and his courtier. He must be coming to try for the examination.

CHILDREN: [*In hushed voices*] The Prince! The Prince! The Prince!

SOUND: *Footsteps.*

COURTIER: [*With impatience*] Ssh—ssh—ssh! Out of the way there! Make way for His Royal Highness!

PRINCE: Well, I see no monks. Am I to be kept waiting here all day?

COURTIER: Your Highness, the hour has not yet—

PRINCE: I say I will not be kept waiting. What will my father, the king, say when he hears I have been kept standing in the highway with a rabble of common peasant children?

COURTIER: Here come Father Anselm—and Father Gregory, Your Highness.

SOUND: *Footsteps.*

GREGORY: Well, well, Brother Anselm—there seems quite a goodly number waiting for us today.

ANSELM: Yes, Brother Gregory. I trust we shall discover the right boys at last. Let me see—I suppose we should examine His Royal Highness first?

GREGORY: Truly, my brother. Let us commit no breach of etiquette.

ANSELM: Your Highness! How old are you?

COURTIER: [*Haughtily*] His Royal Highness has just completed his eleventh year.

ANSELM: Is he diligent? What about his lessons?

COURTIER: He doesn't *need* to study.

GREGORY: Well, well, well, Anselm, I think we must question this paragon.

MUSIC: *Bridge.*

ANSELM: You do know the answers very well. Your Royal Highness is accepted. Now, Brother Gregory, we will contine the examination. First boy!

GREGORY: Your name?

GILBERT: Gilbert. The carpenter's apprentice.

ANSELM: Are you a good boy?

GILBERT: I guess so, sir.

GREGORY: Do you always speak the truth, Gilbert?

GILBERT: [*Stammering*] W-w-well, nearly always.

ANSELM: Tut-tut-tut! That won't do at all. *Always* speak the truth, my boy. I am afraid we can't take you. Are there any more boys?

GREGORY: One boy, Brother Anselm.

ANSELM: Ah, yes! I have seen this boy before, I think. Isn't this boy named Peter?

PETER: Yes, sir.

MISTRESS SPINNING: And a better boy never lived, Your Reverence, if you'll excuse me for mentioning it.

146

ANSELM: Certainly. We shall be very glad to hear what you know about Peter.

MISTRESS SPINNING: It's just this, sir. He's a good, hard-working, honest boy, sir, and very obedient to his parents. He also takes good care of his little lame sister, Rosalia.

GREGORY: Well, well, Brother Anselm, it does seem as if we have found a good boy at last, doesn't it?

ANSELM: Yes, Brother Gregory, this is surely the right boy for us. And now that Peter and the Prince are accepted, let us return to the monastery and resume our exercises there.

MUSIC: *Bridge.*

ANNOUNCER: It is now one week before Christmas, and we hear Peter and the Prince talking together in the garden.

PRINCE: [*Crossly*] Well, I don't see how you can *stand* this place, Peter. I've had more than enough. I'm just sick of it, I am.

PETER: I'm sorry, Your Highness.

PRINCE: Yes, that's what you always say. Why in the world do you keep on working and working? I believe you like it. Come here, I tell you!

SOUND: *Footsteps. Peter comes forward.*

PETER: Well, Your Highness?

PRINCE: That's right, Peter. Now you just tell me what you like about it.

PETER: Why, Your Highness, you know I'm a poor boy and I've always had to work. This is such pretty work —it's just like play. And I really never had enough to eat until I came here to live. I tell you, it's horrid to be hungry! Then the Good Fathers are so kind, and I love the Christmas carols and the chimes—why I think it's a beautiful place, Your Highness. Don't you like to watch the toys grow?

PRINCE: Oh, they grow so slowly. I expected to have a bushelful of new toys every month, and not one have I had yet. I never saw such a stupid place to stay in all my life. I want to have my velvet tunic on and go home to the palace where I can ride on my white pony and hear them all tell me how charming I am.

PETER: Never mind, Your Highness. It's pretty nearly Christmas now, and in a few days the toys will be ready to pick. Come along and I'll help you water those tin soldiers over there. You didn't get that done, did you?

PRINCE: No, and I won't do it, either. As for you, Peter, you're *tame*. If you had a grain of spirit, you'd hate it just as much as I do—

SOUND: *Footsteps as Peter walks away.*

PRINCE: [*Low*] There he goes now to water those horrid soldiers. I won't stay here a bit longer. I'll get that ladder out of the tool house and get over the wall and go home. But I'll take some Christmas presents with me.

PETER: [*Fading out*] I think I see Father Anselm and Father Gregory coming into the garden.

SOUND: *Footsteps.*

ANSELM: Well Gregory, we have every cause to rejoice in the fine flourishing condition of our garden. Peter has kept the beds wonderfully clear of weeds.

GREGORY: Yes, and I think I may say that our garden has never been so fine as this year. It was a happy day for us when we found Peter. Let us give our minds to the contemplation of the doll bed. How lovely the little creatures are!

ANSELM: Why, why, why, what is this? Here is a vacant place!

GREGORY: Oh, yes, Brother, that doll didn't come up. I noticed the place long ago. Let's go on now with our inspection. [*Fading out*]

PETER: [*Fading in—whispers*] Why, Rosalia! How in the world did you get in here?

ROSALIA: I just crept in behind one of the monks. I saw him going along the street, and I ran after him; and when he opened the big gates, I just crept in. I was so lonesome for you, Peter.

PETER: Well, I don't see what I am going to do with you, now you *are* here. I can't let you out again, and I don't know whatever the monks will say!

ROSALIA: Oh, I know! I'll stay out here in the garden. I'll sleep in one of those beautiful dolly-cradles over there, and you can bring me something to eat.

PETER: But the monks come out very often to look over the garden and they'll be sure to find you.

ROSALIA: No, I'll hide. Oh, Peter, see that place where there isn't any dolly?

PETER: Yes, that doll didn't come up.

ROSALIA: I'll tell you what I'll do. I'll just stand here in her place and nobody can tell the difference.

PETER: Well, I suppose you can do that. Of course, I'm glad to see you; but I'm afraid the monks wouldn't like it. Now I must go and put my tools away. Be

149

very quiet, Rosalia, because I see the Prince coming. [*Fading out*]

SOUND: *Footsteps.*

PRINCE: Now, if I can just get down on the other side. Oh, I see some of my father's people riding by! I'll get them to help. My Lord! My Lord! Hither!

SOUND: [*Voices from outside wall*] The Prince! The Prince! His Royal Highness!

PRINCE: I'll just jump.

SOUND: *Thump.*

PRINCE: [*Muffled*] No, I'm not hurt. Let us get away! Hasten, my Lords, hasten!

SOUND: *Voices in distance. Gallop of horses riding by.*

ROSALIA: Oh, what a naughty boy! [*Calling*] Peter! Peter! Oh, Peter, the Prince has run away.

PETER: Run away? I'll go and see. He surely has! There he goes with that gentleman! I was afraid he would try that! But this ladder has always been kept locked up. Oh, too bad—most of the toys are broken. Keep very still, sister. I must put these away and tell the Abbot and Father Anselm, Ambrose, and Hilarion what has happened. [*Fading out*]

SOUND: *Footsteps.*

ANSELM: Why, what is this! I thought that wax doll didn't come up. Can my eyes deceive me? There is a doll here—and what a doll! On crutches and in poor homely gear!

ROSALIA: [*Starting*] Oh!

ANSELM: It is a miracle! The little girl is alive! Parva puella viva est. I must summon the Abbot and the brethren at once. We will pick her and pay her the honors she is entitled to—Hilarion! Brother Hilarion!

SOUND: *Footsteps.*

HILARION: [*Panting*] Did you call, Brother Anselm?

ANSELM: Summon the Holy Father Abbot at once—say to him that it is a matter of great importance.

SOUND: *Footsteps running.*

HILARION: Father Abbot, come quickly!

ABBOT: Yes, what is it? At the wax doll bed, did you say, Hilarion? Ah, yes, there is Anselm.

ANSELM: Most Holy Abbot, behold a miracle. Vide Miraculum! Thou wilt remember that there was one wax doll planted which did not come up. Behold! In its place I have found this doll on crutches, and it is— alive.

ABBOT: Alive, did you say, Anselm! Let me see her!

AMBROSE: I think I can cure this child with my herbs and simples, if Your Reverence wills that I should try.

ABBOT: But I don't know. I never heard of curing a miracle.

AMBROSE: If it is not lawful, my humble power will not suffice to cure it.

ABBOT: True. We will take her, then, and thou shalt exercise thy healing art upon her. I will carry the child. We will go on now with our Christmas devotions, for which we should feel all the more zeal.

SOUND: *Footsteps.*

MUSIC: *Musical curtain.*

ANNOUNCER: It is now Christmas morning. Peter and Rosalia are talking together.

PETER: Oh, sister, I feel so miserable! The good Fathers are so kind that I feel worse than ever. I hate not to tell them the truth about you, and on Christmas day, too. You know they think that you are a live doll, and a miracle, and you're no such thing. You're just Peter's little sister, aren't you pet? And they have been so kind, and Father Ambrose has made your poor little ankle well. So it makes me feel horrid to think we're deceiving them. Why, it's 'most as bad as telling a story.

ROSALIA: Poor Peter, I'm so sorry!

PETER: What shall we do about it, sister?

ROSALIA: Why, Peter, I'll just tell them. They're all so kind, I don't think they will be cross.

PETER: Well, sister, I don't believe they will, either. It's Christmas day, so I want to be sure to do what is right. And this is right—I am sure of that. Now I must run away; I see the monks coming.

SOUND: *Footsteps.*

ABBOT: We'll take our tray of toys to Rosalia.

GREGORY: These are all presents for you—our little miracle.

ROSALIA: Please, I'm not a miracle; I'm only Peter's little sister.

AMBROSE and HILARION: Peter!

ANSELM and GREGORY: Peter's little sister!

152

ABBOT: Peter? The Peter who works in our garden?

ROSALIA: Yes, Peter's little sister.

GREGORY: Surely, here's an opportunity for a whole monastery full of monks to look foolish.

ANSELM: Filing up in procession—

AMBROSE: With our hands full of gifts—

HILARION: And then to find out that this famous miracle is nothing but Peter's little sister.

ABBOT: My children, harken to me. Haven't I always maintained that there are two ways of looking at anything? If an object is not what we wish it to be in one light, let us see if there is not some other light under which it will surely meet our views. This lovely creation is a little girl and not a doll, that is true. She did not come up in the place of the wax doll, and she is not a miracle in that light. But look at her in another light and surely she *is* a miracle. Do you not see? Look at her, the darling little girl! Isn't the very meaning and sweetness of all Christmas in her loving, trusting, innocent little face?

ANSELM: Yes, yes, she is a miracle, a miracle, indeed!

ABBOT: And Peter. Where is Peter?

PETER: Here I am, sir.

ABBOT: Peter, we feel so happy this beautiful Christmas day that we must find some expression for our joy. We must surely find a way to share such happiness with others. Run, my son, open the monastery gates and bid all the village people who wait there for our usual gifts to enter and take part in our pleasure. Think, my children, what a gift we have here for the poor parents of Peter and little Rosalia. This dear little girl will be restored to them, not lame, as she was when she wandered here, but well and strong and happy like other little ones.

SOUND: *Footsteps. Peter goes to gate.*

MUSIC: *Christmas music fading in.*

SOUND: *Footsteps of villagers.*

ABBOT: Welcome, welcome, my good people! A Merry Christmas to you all!

VILLAGERS: Merry Christmas! Merry Christmas!

SOUND: *Opening of letter.*

ABBOT: My children, listen to this. We have here a message from His Majesty, the King. He tells us that his son, the Prince, reached his palace in safety, and that he has come to feel great regret for all the trouble and anxiety he caused the Christmas monks. He hopes that the Prince's repentance, though late, will help to season our Christmas and make it a happy one. And His Majesty adds that he finds great improvement in his son. Well! Well! This does indeed add yet another happiness to our day. And I know you all, little and big, are just as happy as we are; for at last the gates are open to the monastery of the Christmas monks.

MUSIC: *All sing a Christmas carol.*

Jar of Rosemary

From the *Story-teller*, by Maud Lindsay. Published by Lothrop, Lee & Shepard Company. Reproduced by permission of the publishers. Adapted for radio by Katherine Watson. (Grades 3-4)

5 minutes

CAST OF CHARACTERS

PRINCE
QUEEN .... mother of Prince
SERVANT
OLD WOMAN
SICK CHILD .... grandson of old woman
NURSE

SOUNDS

Footsteps
Horses' hoofs
Knocking at door

Door opening
Door closing
Music

Jar of Rosemary

ANNOUNCER: There was once a little Prince whose mother, the Queen, was sick. When autumn came she grew better, and the little Prince was allowed to go into the room and stand beside her bed. We hear him talking to her—

PRINCE: What would you like for a Christmas present, Mother?

QUEEN: What should I like for a Christmas present? A smile and a kiss and a hug around the neck; these are the dearest gifts I know.

PRINCE: Smiles and kisses and hugs you can have every day. Think, Mother, think! If you could choose the thing you wanted most in all the world, what would you take?

QUEEN: If I might take my choice of anything in all the world, I believe a little jar of rosemary like that which bloomed in my mother's window when I was a little girl, would please me better than anything else.

SOUND: *Footsteps.*

SERVANT: Oh! Prince, is there something you wish?

PRINCE: [*To servant*] Will you please go immediately to my father's greenhouse to inquire for a rosemary plant?

SERVANT: There are carnations pink in your father's greenhouses, and roses with golden hearts, and lovely lilies; but there is no rosemary.

PRINCE: Then go into the country for it. No matter where it grows, my mother must have it for a Christmas present.

ANNOUNCER: So messengers went into the country to seek the plant, but each came back to say there was no rosemary. Two days before Christmas, news was brought that rosemary had been found growing in a jar, right in the very city where the Prince lived. We hear the Prince talking to one of the servants—

PRINCE: But where is it? Why have you not brought it with you? Go and get it at once.

SERVANT: Well, as for that, there is a little difficulty. The old woman to whom the rosemary belongs does not want to sell it, even though I offered her a handful of gold and silver. But perhaps if your little Highness would go yourself and ask her, she might change her mind.

PRINCE: Why, I will go right away. Please order the horses.

SOUND: *Horses' hoofs.*

MUSIC: *Bridge.*

PRINCE: Well, here we are.

SOUND: *Knocking—door opening and closing.*

OLD WOMAN: Oh! Prince, I'm glad to see you. Will you come in? My grandson is just your age, but he is sick and cannot play as you do. He would like to see you.

PRINCE: Hello! Wouldn't you like to see my favorite plaything? It's a ball, sort of like magic, and made of gold. See how it bounces!

SICK CHILD: Oh! How beautiful it is! May I just hold it?

OLD WOMAN: My grandson has always wanted a golden ball.

PRINCE: Will you sell the jar of rosemary for my mother's Christmas?

OLD WOMAN: I'm sorry, but I've brought it from the home where I lived as a child and I hope to keep it until I die.

PRINCE: Then I must be going.

SOUND: *Footsteps. Door opening and closing.*

SICK CHILD: Grandmother, if I had such a ball to hold in my hand, I should be contented all day.

OLD WOMAN: You may as well wish for the moon in the sky.

MUSIC: *Musical curtain.*

ANNOUNCER: In the evening she thought of what her grandson had said; and taking the jar of rosemary, the old woman hastened to the king's palace. When she was taken to the Prince, we hear—

OLD WOMAN: Gold and silver would not buy the rosemary; but if you will give me your golden ball for my little grandchild, you may have the plant.

PRINCE: But my ball is the most wonderful ball that was ever made, and it is my favorite plaything. I would not give it away for anything.

ANNOUNCER: And so the old woman had to go home with her jar of rosemary under her shawl. The next day was the day before Christmas. The little Prince went to put his present of a jewel on the Queen's table with her Christmas presents. We hear him talking to his nurse—

158

PRINCE: She wanted a jar of rosemary.

NURSE: Your mother will never think of it again when she sees these things. You may be sure of that.

PRINCE: If I had a rosemary plant I'd be willing to sell it for a purse of gold, wouldn't you?

NURSE: Indeed, yes. And so would anyone in his right senses.

PRINCE: I wish it were spring! It is easy to get rosemary then, isn't it?

NURSE: Your little Highness is like the king's parrot that knows but one word with your rosemary, rosemary, rosemary. Her majesty, the Queen, only asked for it in order to please you.

ANNOUNCER: But the little Prince was not sure. When the nurse had gone to her supper, and he was left alone, he took the ball with him and hastened toward the old woman's house.

SOUND: *Knocking. Door opening.*

OLD WOMAN: Oh! it's your Highness.

SOUND: *Door closing.*

PRINCE: Here is the ball! Please give me the rosemary for my mother.

MUSIC: *Musical curtain.*

ANNOUNCER: And so it happened that when the Queen sat down before her great table of gifts, the first thing she spied was a jar of sweet rosemary.

QUEEN: Oh, I should rather have this than all the other gifts in the world. Thank you, my son.

Lottie's Valentine

From the story, *Lottie's Valentine*, by Katherine Wigmore Eyre.
Published by the Oxford University Press. Reproduced by per-
mission of the publishers. Adapted for radio by Katherine Watson.
(Grades 5-6)   25 minutes

Cast of Characters

LOTTIE .... an orphan, eight years old
THÉRÈSE .... an orphan, ten years old
SISTER URSULA .... head of Convent
JULES .... a neighborhood boy, twelve years old
PAPA DUVAL .... owner of Café de Bon Goût
MAMA DUVAL .... wife

Sounds

Knocking
Slap
Snoring
Door opening and
    closing
Rattle of paper
Stumbling
Music
Rattle of dishes

Running up stairs
Whistle
Horses' hoofs
Footsteps
Jingle of gold coins
Opening of bottle
Clink of glasses

Lottie's Valentine

ANNOUNCER: The setting of Lottie's Valentine is laid in the Convent of the Good Shepherd in New Orleans. We find Lottie, who is eight years old, in the garden after Sister Ursula has dismissed the girls when the long, busy day is nearly over. Ten-year-old Thérèse is also playing in the garden. Lottie does not like her, for she is a tale bearer. It is a cold winter day, and we hear Lottie talking to herself—

LOTTIE: Some day I'll get away from here. I'll get past this gate, and then I'll see for myself what it's like outside. I won't stay here forever. I won't! I won't! Nobody can make me stay!

THÉRÈSE: Hello, Lottie! I was right! I knew I'd find you down here by the gate. I told the girls so, when they asked where you were. Why don't you come and play with us? Aren't you cold? Let's play tag! What's the use of just standing here staring down the road? You do that every day.

LOTTIE: I don't know why, Thérèse. I don't know why I like to look out the gate so much—I just do, that's all. Some day I'll get away from here, and then the gate won't matter any more. There won't be high walls to keep me in any longer. I'll go to town and dance in the street when it's Mardi Gras time, and eat pralines all day long—just as many as I want. I'll get out, I tell you, just wait and see!

THÉRÈSE: Oh, Lottie, how funny you are! You make me laugh! Get away from here? That's a good joke! Wait till I tell the girls! Why, you'll never get away, Lottie! Never, never! Everyone knows that. You

161

haven't any mother or father. You haven't even a Tante Louise, as I have. You haven't a big sister, like Amélie, and a place to go on holidays. You haven't an uncle like Sophie's, who takes her out on Sundays and fête days. You have no one. You were left here when you were a baby. Here you'll have to stay, Lottie, all the rest of your life. Silly Lottie! Silly-billy Lottie! Always staring down the road and making up fine stories to fool yourself.

SOUND: *Lottie shoves and slaps Thérèse.*

LOTTIE: There, take that, you nasty girl, and leave me alone.

THÉRÈSE: [*Falling into a rosebush*] I'll get even with you, Lottie, for this! See if I don't! You'll be sorry, Miss Nobody!

SOUND: *Running—then stumbling.*

LOTTIE: Why, look at this little pigeon. Oh! you poor thing! Where did you come from? How did you happen to fall here, I wonder? Did a hawk pounce on you? Is that why you're so bloody and ruffled? Oh, I hope you aren't going to die. You look dreadfully sick! Oh, dear, I wish I knew how to help you. I wonder what this metal band stamped with numerals and letters around your leg means. Don't try to get away! I won't hurt you—you mustn't be afraid of me. I'll take care of you and make a nice bed for you. When you are well again, I'll let you fly away to your roost, wherever it is. I'm going to ask Sister Ursula if I may keep you in my room.

MUSIC: *Bridge.*

SOUND: *Footsteps. Knocking at door.*

LOTTIE: You see, Sister Ursula, it's just a bird that's hurt and can't fly. A poor little cold pigeon that I found out on the garden path. May I please keep the pigeon until it is well? I'll make a bed for it. And could I have some dishes for crumbs and water?

SISTER URSULA: You may keep the pigeon, Lottie. It was good of you to take pity on the poor thing, and I don't see any reason why you should not have it until it is well enough to fly away. Come along. We will take the pigeon to your room. Here are the dishes, but be careful of them.

SOUND: *Rattle of dishes.*

LOTTIE: Oh, thank you, Sister Ursula—thank you for letting me keep the pigeon.

SOUND: *Footsteps of Lottie and Sister Ursula going to Lottie's room.*

SISTER URSULA: Get me your sponge, child. I'll wash the blood off the poor thing's breast. What a dreadful wound. A hawk must surely have pounced on it. Somehow the pigeon got free from its claws, I imagine, and tried to fly to its home, but was so exhausted that it fell here in our garden. Look, Lottie, at this band around its leg! I don't know what the numerals and letters stand for, but I do know that the band means the bird is a homing pigeon with a loft and an owner somewhere. The kindest thing for you to do is to care for it now, and then let it fly away again just as soon as it grows stronger. There, now, I've washed it well—the wound is clean. Give me your towel, please, and I will dry my hands. Take the pigeon and put it in the box again. Keep it warm and well fed, and perhaps you will save its life, after all. You are a good child, my dear, a real little Samaritan. Now I must go, and you must get ready for supper. The bell will ring any minute.

SOUND: *Footsteps of Sister Ursula receding.*

LOTTIE: Never, never have I been so happy. Never before in all my life. This pigeon is the only thing that ever really belonged to me.

MUSIC: *Musical curtain.*

ANNOUNCER: Three hours' drive from the Convent of the Good Shepherd is the Café de Bon Gôut, run by Papa and Mama Duval. Papa also has a pigeon loft and has several homing pigeons. The one called Coo-Coo is Papa Duval's favorite. We hear young Jules, a neighbor boy of twelve years, who helps the Duvals in their Café and also cleans the perches of the birds, talking to Mama Duval—

JULES: Brr, it's cold. But it is warm here in your kitchen, Mama Duval, and I smell something good. Mama, what is the matter? You look worried and so sad. Has something gone wrong?

MAMA DUVAL: Oh, it isn't your fault, Jules; it isn't anything you have done. You're a good boy. But oh, I'm so worried over poor Papa. He is in a bad way. Poor Michel! You run upstairs and see what you can do to cheer him. Papa is not ill, but his heart is broken. Coo-Coo is lost. Michel let her out of the loft last night as usual to stretch her wings before bed-time, but she didn't come back. Michel waited for her all night. Something very bad has surely happened to that Coo-Coo, for never before has she stayed away like this. And Papa is like a crazy man, I tell you. Nothing I say is of any use. You go up and talk to him, Jules.

164

Jules: Papa Duval, Mama has told me what happened. Oh, I'm so sorry. But please don't look so sad! Surely Coo-Coo will come back safely. And even if she doesn't come back, Papa, even if she is dead; there are plenty of other birds for you to raise. The loft is full of young ones coming along.

Papa Duval: No, Jules, there is no use your talking. It's no use at all for you and Mama to tell me that Coo-Coo will come home. She is dead. My poor blue beauty. Some imbecile hunter has shot her to bits or a hawk has grabbed her. Oh, well, I'll have to forget about her, I suppose. I'll have to put her out of my mind and think only about the other birds. Perhaps I'll raise a winner from them some day, but never will there be another champion like my blue queen. Oh, Coo-Coo, what has happened to you? Why don't you fly home to Michel, eh?

Music: *Musical curtain.*

Announcer: Lottie, however, didn't know that the blue pigeon she had found was the beloved favorite of Papa Duval's flock, nor that the jolly little restaurant keeper in New Orleans grieved every day for his lost Coo-Coo. But Lottie, who had never been beyond the iron gates of the convent, valued freedom; so on Valentine's Day, she sent the pigeon, healed at last, winging its way back home. Tied to its leg was her newly-made valentine, an appealing message of love and friendship. Jules is alone in the loft of the Café when Coo-Coo, with a rush of wings, flies in the trap door.

Jules: Papa Duval, Papa, come quickly! Coo-Coo is back! Coo-Coo is safe! Do your hear me? Come quickly, she's here in the loft, Papa!

Footsteps of Papa and Mama Duval running upstairs.

Papa Duval: Coo-Coo, my little Coo-Coo, my blue beauty, where have you been all this time? What happened to you, my little queen? Shame on you, Coo-Coo, for making me worry so much! Why did you not fly home to me, eh? But I'm not going to scold you, little champion. No, no! I am too happy to waste breath on scoldings!

Jules: Look! What's this tied to her leg, Papa? What can it be?

Papa Duval: Why, it's a red heart, a valentine. It says: "Please let me be your valentine. I am eight years old. I live at the Convent of the Good Shepherd. My name is Lottie." I don't know what it means, Mama.

Mama Duval: One thing we know, at any rate—the Convent of the Good Shepherd is out on the Bayou Road. It's the place where the nuns take poor and homeless children.

Papa Duval: I know, yes, of course, I know where it is! But what has that got to do with us? How did she get hold of Coo-Coo in the first place, this Lottie child, and why does she send us a valentine? Can you answer that one?

Mama Duval: She says she is eight years old. That is too little to have no other home but a convent. It is no life for a child. The nuns are kind. They are very good, but they cannot be mother and father to all the homeless little ones that come to their gate.

Jules: I bet she doesn't have food to eat like yours, Mama.

Mama Duval: I feel sorry for her, let me tell you, not having any mother or father.

PAPA DUVAL: She must be thanked for sending Coo-Coo safely back to us. Yes, she must be thanked and rewarded. The very first day that we can leave the Café, we must go to the Convent and see her.

MAMA DUVAL: You are right, Michel. The very first chance, we will go. It is easy to see that the child, whoever she is, has a good heart or else she would not have let Coo-Coo go free. It is all very strange, this affair, and it is too bad that Coo-Coo cannot speak and tell us what happened.

JULES: Mama Duval, Papa Duval, listen to me one little minute, please. Do not think me impertinent, but if that Lottie girl is lonely and has no one; if the Convent is her only home, why do you not bring her here to live at the Bon Goût? You could teach her to cook, Mama. She would be most useful. When you are old, she could take your place. And if you took her in and loved her, that little Lottie, only eight years old, would not have to send any more valentines through the air tied to a pigeon's leg.

SOUND: *Jules flees. Door slams.*

PAPA DUVAL: Pouf, pouf, is he mad? Has Coo-Coo's return and all the excitement made him soft in the head?

MUSIC: *Musical curtain.*

ANNOUNCER: A week has gone by and we hear Mama and Papa Duval who have just gone to bed—

PAPA DUVAL: Move over and make room for me, my little cabbage.

MAMA DUVAL: It is you, Michel, who are fat, and who takes up all the room. But if you will listen to me and pay attention to what I say, I will not care about your

167

pulling off the blankets. It is about that petite Lottie that I wish to speak, Michel. Here it is, a whole week since Coo-Coo flew home, and still we have done nothing to thank her. Every day we have been too busy. But now the time has come! Tomorrow is my birthday, and you must give me a present. And the best present of all, Michel, would be just what Jules said to us. Yes, I have been thinking it over all week. That boy is not crazy. He is very sensible. I want Lottie— I want to bring her here. And if we like her, if she is a nice little one, if she is happy with us, perhaps we can keep her always. Now! You have heard me! I mean what I say, Papa!

PAPA DUVAL: Nonsense, Mama! Utter nonsense! Go to sleep! Never have I heard such a crazy idea! A gold brooch for your birthday would be one thing, or a new silk dress—but a Lottie child! A strange child to come here and live? Never! Coo-Coo is back, and I am grateful—and if you wish, we will close up the Café tomorrow and go to the Convent to thank this child. But there the matter stops.

SOUND: *Papa Duval snoring.*

MAMA DUVAL: Wake up, Michel! You'll make me **very** happy if you'll let me have Lottie.

PAPA DUVAL: Do you wish this very much? All right, then.

MAMA DUVAL: Oh! Papa, now you've said yes—I'm very happy. I wish this more than anything in the world. Lottie will have the little empty room under the eaves and because business is so good, there will be no trouble at all to keep her warm and give her plenty to eat and nice clothes to wear. Anybody with sense knows that eight years old is too little to be homeless!

MUSIC: *Musical curtain.*

ANNOUNCER: It is now the next day, and we hear Mama Duval talking to Jules—

MAMA DUVAL: Jules, we are leaving at once for a trip to the Convent and if all goes well, we will bring Lottie back with us to live at the Café de Bon Goût.

JULES: Oh, I'm glad! That is very fine, indeed, Mama! What a lot of fun I'll have playing with that little one! I'll show her the goats! I'll make a wagon and hitch them so she can drive!

MAMA DUVAL: Never mind, Jules. Stop chattering! A goat cart indeed! If that Lottie child comes here, she works hard, understand? Now go whistle for a cab! We can't stand wasting time like this. What has come over us, I'm sure I don't know. That Coo-Coo and that Lottie have upset us head over heels. Fetch a cab and I'll hurry and put on my best dress. It's high time we started on this wild goose chase. Oh! I mustn't forget the macaroons for her. And don't forget your gold coins, Michel!

SOUND: *Cab arrives. Horses' hoofs.*

JULES: Good-by, Mama! Good-by, Papa! Good luck to you! Don't worry about anything. I'll feed the pigeons and look after everything. Au revoir, au revoir!

MUSIC: *Bridge.*

SOUND: *Horses' hoofs.*

PAPA DUVAL: Well, here we are at the Convent.

SOUND: *Footsteps. Knocking at door. Door opening and closing.*

PAPA DUVAL: Sister Ursula?

MAMA DUVAL: Now, Papa, tell Sister the whole story.

PAPA DUVAL: Well, you see my Coo-Coo—[*Fading out*]

MUSIC: *Bridge.*

SISTER URSULA: What a curious story! So you've come to see Lottie. I'll go and call her.

SOUND: *Footsteps.*

LOTTIE: [*Fading in*] Visitors for me, Sister Ursula? Oh, no, there must be some mistake. There could not be visitors for me. For Sophie or Amélie or Thérèse, perhaps, but not for me, because I have no one in all the world.

SISTER URSULA: Do as I say, Lottie! Make yourself tidy! Sometimes *le bon Dieu* sends us friends when we least expect them.

SOUND: *Footsteps going downstairs.*

LOTTIE: Oh! How do you do!

SOUND: *Rattle of paper bag.*

MAMA DUVAL: Some macaroons for you, petite. Eat them all, for they are good.

SOUND: *Jingle of gold coins.*

PAPA DUVAL: Some gold coins for you, Mademoiselle Lottie. For you because you were kind to my Coo-Coo. Because you took care of my beautiful pigeon and sent her safely home. Ah, yes, little one. We know all about it, from Sister Ursula here. And my thanks to you, Mademoiselle, with all my heart.

SISTER URSULA: Listen to me, child. Once you were left at the gates here long ago. You were not wanted. You were wrapped in rags. No one knew where you came from, nor to whom you belonged. But today, Lottie, you will go out through that same gate into a new life. Now you are wanted! You will be loved! You will belong to Mama and Papa Duval, and they will belong to you. Tell me, Lottie, do you want to go and live with them? Do you think you will be happy with them? It is your choice to make, my dear.

LOTTIE: Yes, Sister Ursula, I want to go with them. I want to belong to them.

SISTER URSULA: Then it is all settled. Now, run to your room and pack your clothes, Lottie. You must not keep these good people waiting.

SOUND: *Footsteps to Lottie's room.*

LOTTIE: Oh, how wonderful! I'm going to belong to someone. I'm so very happy.

MUSIC: *Bridge.*

SOUND: *Footsteps.*

LOTTIE: Good-by, Sister Ursula.

SISTER URSULA: [*Kissing her*] Good-by, Lottie.

LOTTIE: Good-by, girls.

SOUND: *Horses' hoofs.*

ANNOUNCER: It was all just as Lottie had dreamed so many times. And then, at last, they were in front of the Café de Bon Goût. Jules was waiting for them at the gate.

171

JULES: Hello, hello, hello, Mademoiselle Lottie. So you're our valentine girl, are you? I knew they'd bring you back with them. I knew they'd like you. Welcome to the Café de Bon Goût! At your service, Mademoiselle, at your service!

LOTTIE: [*Laughing*] That funny boy! But he is nice. I know we will be good friends.

MAMA DUVAL: Come along now. Come along, cherie. It is late. We have had a long drive. Now, Jules, no more of your capering and fooling! Plenty of time for play tomorrow! Lottie must have supper and then go to bed.

LOTTIE: Oh! I want to see Coo-Coo.

SOUND: *Footsteps.*

LOTTIE: Oh! I think she remembers me. See, she takes the rice from my hand. Oh, you darling little bird, I love you! I love you! How good you were to carry my valentine! How can I ever thank you enough?

MAMA DUVAL: [*Calling*] Supper, supper, come down to supper! Lottie, Michel, and you, Jules.

SOUND: *Footsteps.*

MUSIC: *Bridge.*

LOTTIE: Oh, what a feast! This chicken with rice is so good. And these pancakes rolled in jelly. What good almonds and cheese!

PAPA DUVAL: [*Opening bottle of wine—clink of glasses*] We'll have to celebrate Mama's birthday having some wine. Many, many happy returns of the day, Mama— and after that, welcome to you, Lottie. Come, we shall all drink to Lottie.

172

LOTTIE: Oh! What fun this is!

PAPA DUVAL: Here is to Coo-Coo. Here is to my little queen, the champion of them all! Here is to the luck of the Café de Bon Goût. May we never be parted!

MAMA DUVAL: Time for bed! Come along, Lottie. That's a good child. You, Jules, clear the table.

SOUND: *Footsteps.*

MAMA DUVAL: And here is your little bed, Lottie, under the eaves. Now I'll tuck you in and give you a good-night kiss.

LOTTIE: [*Joyfully*] Good night! Good night, Mama! Good night, Papa! Good night, Jules! Good night, everybody! Oh, I'm very happy! I like it here so much. I am just like Coo-Coo. I've flown safely home.

The Country Bunny and the Little Gold Shoes

From the book, *The Country Bunny and the Little Gold Shoes*, by DuBose Heyward. Published by Houghton Mifflin Company. Reproduced by permission of the publishers and author. Adapted for radio by Katherine Watson. (Grades 3-4)   10 minutes

CAST OF CHARACTERS

COUNTRY GIRL BUNNY
COUNTRY MOTHER BUNNY
GRANDFATHER BUNNY

SOUNDS

Footsteps of bunnies   Music
Running of bunnies   Opening of door

174

The Country Bunny and the Little Gold Shoes

ANNOUNCER: We hear of the Easter bunny who comes each Easter day before sunrise to bring eggs for boys and girls, so we think there is only one bunny. But this is not so. There are really five Easter bunnies. When one of them grows old and can no longer run fast, the kind grandfather bunny who lives at the Palace of Easter Eggs calls the bunnies together from the whole world to select the very best one to take his place. We now hear a little country girl bunny—

COUNTRY GIRL BUNNY: Some day I shall grow up to be an Easter bunny—you wait and see! You needn't laugh at me and tell me to go back to the country. You just wait and see!

ANNOUNCER: The little girl cottontail grew up to be a young lady cottontail. And by and by she had a husband; and then one day, much to her surprise, there were twenty-one cottontail babies to take care of.

COUNTRY MOTHER BUNNY: Now, children, since I have such a lovely big family, I guess I'll have to stop thinking about being an Easter bunny and hopping over the world with lovely eggs for little boys and girls, and take care of my babies. But because you're such bright little bunnies, we are going to have some fun. I'll teach you two bunnies to sweep the cottage. You two I'll teach how to make beds. You two go to the kitchen and learn how to cook a good dinner. And we'll need two little dish-washers to make the glasses shine like crystal. Two more of you can have these little wash-tubs full of soapsuds to wash all the linen. Two can do the sewing and mending. You two have such sweet voices that you will have to learn to sing. Two more can learn to dance; and then you four can amuse the other bunnies while they work, so they will be gay and happy. Oh! The garden must be looked after, so you two dig in the garden. Now you two take these paints and crayons so you can make pretty pictures for the walls. Why, dear me, there is one of my bunnies left who looks sad and lonely. You are the most polite of my children, so I shall make you keeper of my chair. Whenever I come to dinner, you shall seat me politely at the table.

ANNOUNCER: Then one day, when the little rabbits were half grown, we hear the mother bunny talking to her children—

COUNTRY MOTHER BUNNY: I've just heard that one of the five Easter bunnies is now too slow to deliver the eggs on Easter, so we will go to the Palace of Easter Eggs to watch Grandfather pick out a new one to take his place. How I wish I could be chosen! But that can't happen—because I'm an old Mother bunny.

SOUND: *Footsteps of bunnies going to palace.*

MUSIC: *Bridge.*

COUNTRY MOTHER BUNNY: Oh, see! There's kind, wise Grandfather Bunny. Let's stay here and watch.

GRANDFATHER: Now, all you bunnies will take turns in running and jumping. Get ready—*Go!*

SOUND: *Running of bunnies.*

GRANDFATHER: Yes, you are pretty and you are fast, but you have not shown me that you are either kind or wise. Why bless me, look at little cottontail Mother

176

with all her children. What a large family you have, my dear! I suppose they take all of your time.

COUNTRY MOTHER BUNNY: They did when they were babies, but now they are so well trained that they do most of the work for me.

GRANDFATHER: Ah, you must be very wise to have trained twenty-one children so well. But, tell me, do they always look so happy, and do they always hold their ears up so prettily?

COUNTRY MOTHER BUNNY: Indeed they do! We never have a tear or a cross word in our little country cottage. And if I do say it myself, they do carry their ears better than most bunnies.

GRANDFATHER: Then you must be very kind indeed to have such a happy home. It is too bad that you have had no time to run and grow swift, as I might then have made you my fifth Easter bunny.

COUNTRY MOTHER BUNNY: [*Whispers*] Let's show Grandfather how fast we can run.

SOUND: *Running of bunnies.*

GRANDFATHER: Why, I see that you are swift also. It is too bad that you cannot carry my eggs, because I suppose you will have to stay at home to take care of your children.

COUNTRY MOTHER BUNNY: They can take better care of the house than I. These two are my sweepers. They keep the cottage as clean as your hand. These make the beds without a wrinkle. These cook my dinner. These wash the dishes. These tend the garden. These wash and dry all the clothes. These do the mending. These sing, and the other two dance to keep us merry while we work. These are learning to paint pretty

177

pictures for our walls. And this littlest one of all always pulls out my chair for me when I sit at the table. So you see I can leave them to take care of the house until I come home.

GRANDFATHER: You have proved yourself to be not only wise and kind and swift, but also very clever. Come to the palace tomorrow afternoon, for that is Easter Eve, and you shall be my fifth Easter bunny.

MUSIC: *Musical curtain.*

ANNOUNCER: The next evening Mother Cottontail knocked on the big front door and was admitted to the palace. There she stood in her funny country clothes, but none of the other four Easter bunnies laughed, for they were wise and kind and knew better. They showed her all over the palace, from room to room all piled high with eggs of gold and silver, chocolate eggs, marshmallow eggs, eggs for rich children and eggs for poor children, for children who were sick and children who were well, all over the world.

GRANDFATHER: Now it's time to fill your baskets with Easter eggs and be on your way.

MUSIC: *Bridge.*

GRANDFATHER: Little Mother Cottontail, I know you are tired. You have been filling those baskets for over an hour, but I want you to see this egg. Peek through, and tell me what you see.

COUNTRY MOTHER BUNNY: Why, I see a beautiful scene with a sleigh and a lake with people skating on the ice. Oh! How pretty it is!

GRANDFATHER: Because you have such a loving heart for children, I am going to give you the best, but the hardest trip of all. Far off, over two rivers and three

178

mountains, there is a great mountain peak. And in a little cottage on that peak is a little boy who has been ill for a whole year. He has been so brave that never once has he cried or complained. The mountain is so high that there is ice on the top. It will be hard to climb, but if you get there, you will give more happiness than any other Easter bunny by taking him this beautiful Easter egg that glitters like a diamond.

ANNOUNCER: Mother Cottontail picked up the egg very gently and went hopping away on her journey. She climbed over the first mountain and then another and yet another until at last she reached the highest mountain of all. She was very tired when at last she reached the ice and snow. Now she was almost to the top and she could see the little cottage all covered with snow where the little boy was sleeping Then a terrible thing happened. Her foot slipped. Down she came until she rolled across a pasture, and finally struck against an apple tree. There she lay, and we hear—

COUNTRY MOTHER BUNNY: Oh! My leg pains me. I wonder if I can go on. I just must, for in a few minutes it will be daylight, and the little boy will be sad if I don't get his Easter egg to him. Why, I thought someone touched my shoulder. Oh, hello, Grandfather.

GRANDFATHER: I surprised you, didn't I, Mother Cottontail? You are not only wise and kind and swift, but you are the bravest of all the bunnies. I shall make you my very own gold-shoe Easter bunny. Let me put these gold shoes on your feet.

COUNTRY MOTHER BUNNY: Why, the pain in my leg is all gone! I'm sure now that I can climb the mountain.

ANNOUNCER: Then, before she knew what was happening, she felt a sudden motion and found herself flying high in the air, until finally she landed right at the cottage door. Quickly she squeezed through a tiny crack and placed the egg in the hand of the beautiful sleeping boy. And just as the Easter morning sun rose, she hopped quickly back to the palace where she found her little basket of eggs for her own family.

COUNTRY MOTHER BUNNY: I must hurry home now with the pretty Easter eggs for my little bunnies, for they, too, must have a happy Easter.

MUSIC: *Musical curtain.*

SOUND: *Opening of door. Footsteps of Mother Bunny.*

COUNTRY MOTHER BUNNY: Sure enough! Everything is in fine order. The floors are nicely swept. There are two lovely new pictures painted and hung on the wall. The dishes are clean and shining. The clothes are washed and mended and neatly hung up. My twenty-one children are all sound asleep in their little beds. Oh! What a happy Easter we are going to have!

ANNOUNCER: And now you can always tell little Mother Cottontail's house from all the others because of the tiny gold shoes hanging on a very special hook in a special place on the wall.

The Baker's Top-Hat Bunny

From the story by Robert L. Grimes published in *Jack and Jill Magazine*. Reproduced by permission of the author. Adapted for radio by Katherine Watson. (Grades 4-5) 10 minutes

CAST OF CHARACTERS

MR. OOFENDORF .... Baker

HIS WIFE

MAN ⎫
LADY ⎪
MESSENGER BOY ⎬ .... Customers
SMALL BOY ⎪
SMALL GIRL ⎭

SOUNDS

Rattling of paper Door opening and closing
Laying hammer down Wrapping of package
Footsteps Music
Tinkle of bell

The Baker's Top-Hat Bunny

ANNOUNCER: This is the story of a Danish baker, Mr. Oofendorf, who owns a little bakery and candy shop. He and his wife live in the back of the store and she helps him with his baking. The next Sunday is Easter and we hear Mr. Oofendorf saying to his wife—

MR. OOFENDORF: We're sure to have a busy time this Easter week.

WIFE: Yes, that's right, and you'd better make loads of cake and candy eggs. We must make lots of money.

MR. OOFENDORF: [*To himself*] Money isn't everything. We all think too much of it.

MUSIC: *Musical curtain.*

ANNOUNCER: For several days, the baker worked hard in his shop. He made hot-cross buns, pies, butter cookies, chocolate bunnies and a whole bushel basketful of candy Easter eggs. All of these things he put into just one of his store windows. The other window he left empty. His wife couldn't understand this, and we hear her saying—

WIFE: But this window has nothing in it. That's no way to make money.

MR. OOFENDORF: I'm working on something very special for that window.

WIFE: And what will that be?

MR. OOFENDORF: It will show my idea of Easter.

WIFE: Silly man! Everyone knows that Easter is for selling hams, fresh eggs, and bakery goods. For making money.

MR. OOFENDORF: No, that isn't what Easter stands for.

MUSIC: *Musical curtain.*

ANNOUNCER: On Good Friday, the one shop window was still bare. But early Saturday morning, after hurrying about and trotting back and forth from kitchen to window, we hear Mr. Oofendorf calling to his wife—

SOUND: *Rattling of paper, laying hammer down.*

MR. OOFENDORF: Come and see. This is my idea of Easter!

SOUND: *Wife's footsteps approaching.*

WIFE: Well! For land's sake! So this is your idea of Easter. All I can see is a big nest of paper grass with a chocolate Easter egg sitting in it. Who ever heard of a winking Easter rabbit made of cake, poking his head out of an egg like that, and wearing a top-hat? It's silly, that's what it is! How much do you think you can get for it?

MR. OOFENDORF: I thought maybe two dollars—

WIFE: What! Two dollars! Why, you've put more than two dollars' worth of good cake in that window, besides your hours and hours of work. Two dollars, indeed! You'd better ask ten dollars.

MR. OOFENDORF: Yes, my dear. I'll make a ten-dollar price tag for it.

WIFE: And sell it to the very first customer that comes in. I must get on with my baking.

SOUND: *Footsteps of wife fading out.*

MR. OOFENDORF: I'm not so anxious to sell the bunny. I'd like people to see it in my window and to understand how I feel about Easter.

SOUND: *Tinkle of bell as front door opens and closes.*

MR. OOFENDORF: Good morning, sir. What can I do for you?

MAN: [*Crossly*] I want a box of that chocolate candy in the window, for my children. That's all Easter ever amounts to at our house. Candy, candy, candy.

SOUND: *Wrapping of package.*

MR. OOFENDORF: Here you are, sir. That'll be one dollar.

SOUND: *Tinkle of bell as door opens and closes.*

MR. OOFENDORF: [*To himself*] My wife thinks Easter is for making money. And that man's children think Easter is for getting lots of candy. Hmm. [*Louder*] Will you please bring me some more chocolate candy for the window, wife?

SOUND: *Wife's footsteps approaching.*

WIFE: Any customers yet for that winking Easter rabbit?

MR. OOFENDORF: No, not yet, my dear. But there will be. In the big crowds on the streets this afternoon, someone will know the meaning of the Easter bunny and want to buy him.

MUSIC: *Musical curtain.*

ANNOUNCER: It is afternoon now and still no one has come into the little bakery to buy the bunny. It has begun to rain. People hurry along—hats pulled down, umbrellas held low. No one has been interested in a top-hat Easter rabbit. But now a woman with a discontented look is coming down the street. She pauses in front of the little shop window and then goes into the store.

SOUND: *Tinkle of bell as door opens and closes.*

MR. OOFENDORF: Something for you, Madame?

LADY: I've come to look at your cakes.

MR. OOFENDORF: Would you care to buy the top-hat bunny? It's ten dollars.

LADY: [*Haughtily*] If I had ten dollars, I'd buy myself a new hat and gloves.

MR. OOFENDORF: But the hat and gloves you are wearing look very nice.

LADY: They're all right to wear on a Saturday shopping trip, but tomorrow is Easter, and if I had a new hat, I could go walking to show off my fine clothes. I don't think I want anything after all. [*Emphatically*] Good day.

SOUND: *Tinkle of bell as door opens and closes.*

MR. OOFENDORF: [*To himself*] Easter isn't for making money, and it isn't just for candy, and it isn't for showing-off.

SOUND: *Wife's footsteps approaching.*

WIFE: Haven't you sold that Easter bunny yet?

MR. OOFENDORF: No, but I like it in the window. It shows—

WIFE: That's what you keep saying. But *what* does it show?

MR. OOFENDORF: [*Sadly*] You really don't see, do you? But just wait. Some customer will understand the meaning of the top-hat bunny.

WIFE: Understand it? We will be better off if someone buys it.

SOUND: *Footsteps fading out. Tinkle of bell as door opens and closes.*

MR. OOFENDORF: Good afternoon and what can I do for you, my boy?

MESSENGER BOY: Could I please have two cupcakes? This gives me a chance to rest and am I tired! Being a messenger boy just before Easter is no cinch. And I still have to go to the other end of town with these Easter lilies and cut flowers.

MR. OOFENDORF: Are all those cut flowers you are carrying for one house?

MESSENGER BOY: Yep—all for one house!

MR. OOFENDORF: [*To himself*] Easter isn't for getting loads of flowers either.

MESSENGER BOY: Whatcha say, mister?

MUSIC: *Musical curtain.*

ANNOUNCER: It is still raining. As the baker watches the rain, a thin-faced boy, shabbily dressed, and his little sister come to the window. Their noses are pressed against the pane and their eyes are big as saucers as

186

they look at the top-hat bunny. It is almost evening now. The youngsters are all excited and decide to go into the shop.

SOUND: *Tinkle of bell as door opens and closes.*

MR. OOFENDORF. Hello, children, and what would you like?

SMALL BOY: Mother gave us a dime for Easter eggs. She says we can pick them out while she goes to the grocery store.

SMALL GIRL: Oh! Look at all these pretty eggs.

MR. OOFENDORF: I saw you children looking at the top-hat bunny. Do you like him?

SMALL BOY: Oh! I think he's wonderful. We came in just to see him. You know we've made up a story about that bunny.

MR. OOFENDORF: Oh! Is that so? Tell me about it, won't you?

SMALL BOY: Well, the broken chocolate egg stands for winter, which is over. The top-hat and the bunny's wink mean that you should always dress as nice as you can, and be jolly. The green of the nest means that spring will soon be here, and there'll be lots of nice things for us in the garden. It's Easter—and spring!

MR. OOFENDORF: Bless me, if that isn't just my idea of Easter too. You ought to buy that top-hat bunny.

SMALL BOY: Oh! We couldn't. The tag says ten dollars.

MR. OOFENDORF: Dear me, does it say that? What a mistake! I wrote a dollar sign and it should be cents. Here, I'll erase it.

SMALL BOY: Ten cents for the top-hat bunny! Gee, can we have him?

MR. OOFENDORF: Why, yes, I think he's been waiting just for you.

MUSIC: *Musical curtain.*

SOUND: *Wife's footsteps approaching.*

WIFE: So you've sold the rabbit at last! Who bought it?

MR. OOFENDORF: A young gentleman and his sister. And they knew what the top-hat bunny stood for.

WIFE: Did you get ten dollars for it?

MR. OOFENDORF: [*Happily*] I sold the bunny for ten cents. Money isn't everything. Candy and new clothes and flowers aren't everything, either. But spring is here, new life is coming to the world. And that's practically everything at Easter time.

The Moffats

From the book, *The Moffats*, by Eleanor Estes. Published by the Harcourt, Brace & Company. Reproduced by permission of the publishers. Adapted for radio by Katherine Watson. (Grades 5-6)

10 minutes

CAST OF CHARACTERS

MAMA

JANE .... her nine-year-old daughter

JOE .... her twelve-year-old son

RUFUS .... her five-and-a-half-year-old son

SYLVIE .... her fifteen-year old daughter

PETER FROST .... a neighbor boy

SOUNDS

Footsteps	Howling of cat
Door opening and closing	Screaming
Running	Stumbling
Groaning noise of trap-door	Sound of chains

The Moffats

ANNOUNCER: This is the story of a family, not poverty-stricken, but just poor. There are four young Moffats, from five-and-a-half year old Rufus to Sylvie, fifteen; Mama, who is a dressmaker and uses a dress form called Madame-the-bust; and, last but not least, Catherine-the-cat. Mostly we see things through the eyes of nine-year-old Janey, and her viewpoint is never commonplace. There is great excitement in the little house on New Dollar Street, for tonight is Halloween. Janey has just come home from school and runs out to join Rufus and Joe in the barn. We hear—

JANE: Are you gettin' ready for tonight?

JOE: You bet! Sylvie said we'd make a ghost. We're going to put her in the attic an' scare Peter Frost.

JANE: When?

JOE: Tonight.

JANE: Ooh! Think of a ghost in the attic! Are you sure Peter Frost will come?

JOE: Oh, sure. He said to me, "Ghosts! Ha-ha! Ghosts! No such thing!" And I said to him, "Sure, in our attic there's a ghost."

JANE: What did he say to that?

JOE: He said, "Ghosts, nothin'."

JANE: What did you say then?

JOE: I said, "All right, if you don't believe me, come on over to our house at eight o'clock, and we'll show you."

190

Rufus: Well, we better get busy. What do we do first?

Joe: First we have to carve the head. This ghost is going to have a pumpkin head. See, this one will do. Let's get busy! Gee, but I hope we scare Peter Frost good. Remember that time he made Rufus fall off the hitchin' post? Remember that time he told Jane to put her mouth up against the hole in the fence and he would give her a piece of candy and he gave her a mouthful of sand instead?

Jane: Remember how he is always pullin' Sylvie's curls every chance he gets? And hard—so it hurts.

Joe: Remember that time he almost got Jane arrested and she had to hide in the bread-box?

Rufus: We should fix him. I know what! We can use my teeth in this head.

Joe: Oh, do you have some teeth?

Rufus: Sure. I'll get them. They are up in the loft, where I keep my treasures. Some of them are my baby teeth, but most of the collection I found under the Grape Room window. You know, Dr. Witty, who lived in our house before we did, was a dentist, and after pulling a tooth, he just tossed it out of the window.

Jane: Well, hurry and get them.

Rufus: All right.

Sound: *Footsteps upstairs fading out. Silence for a few seconds.*

Jane: [*Calling*] Rufus, what are you doin' up there?

Sound: *Footsteps downstairs fading in.*

RUFUS: Comin'. Here they are.

JANE: Gee, these teeth are swell. Look at that big one, will you?

RUFUS: Yeh. Old Natby the blacksmith gave me that one. He said he'd been shoein' an old mare one day and that tooth fell out of her mouth. He said it was the biggest he'd ever seen. Let's put the teeth in the pumpkin. Phew! She looks gruesome with that old horse's tooth hanging over her lower lip.

SYLVIE: [*Calling from distance*] Rufus, Jane, Joe.

RUFUS: Oh! there's Sylvie calling us to supper.

MUSIC: *Bridge.*

JANE: [*Whispering*] Sylvie, have you had a chance to bring Madame-the-bust upstairs?

SYLVIE: [*Whispering*] Not yet. There's plenty of time.

JANE: [*Whispering*] Plenty of time! Supposin' Peter Frost comes before everything's ready? Sh! here comes Mama.

MAMA: I see no reason, even if it is Halloween, why I shouldn't leave you four children. Mrs. Pudge wants me to talk over plans for her silver wedding anniversary dress, so I think I'll go tonight. Now, don't be gallivanting through the streets after eight o'clock. And, Joey, please tie the garbage pail to the back porch or some of those street hoodlums will be trying to tie it to the lamp post. And see that the rake and anything else that's movable is locked in the barn. I won't be very late. Good-by.

SOUND: *Door opening and closing.*

192

SYLVIE: Well, we'd better hurry. First the pumpkin. Who'll get that? You go, Jane and Joe.

SOUND: *Footsteps fading out.*

MUSIC: *Bridge.*

SOUND: *Footsteps fading in.*

JANE: Here's the pumpkin.

SYLVIE: Now the Madame. What's the matter with you tonight, Catherine-the-cat?

JANE: Look at her. She's watchin' and watchin' us.

SYLVIE: Let her watch. I'll take Mrs. Shoemaker's white satin gown from Madame-the-bust before I take her to the attic. You carry the pumpkin, Joe. And Rufus, you bring the scooter. Jane can bring the sheets.

SOUND: *Footsteps upstairs.*

MUSIC: *Bridge.*

JANE: Goodness, all of these stuffed animals of Dr. Witty's make this place spooky. O-o-h, there's Catherine-the-cat. She scared me. We'll put Madame on the scooter and drape the sheets around her. Let's tie one end of this rope to the scooter and make a loop on the other end so we can pull the ghost around.

SYLVIE: All right. Now let's see how she looks.

JOE: Phew!

RUFUS: Boy, oh boy!

JANE: Oh, come on, let's go downstairs. I'm cold.

SOUND: *Footsteps.*

RUFUS: Gee, but this stove feels good.

SOUND: *Door opening and closing.*

PETER FROST: Hey there, Moffats. Where's your old ghost?

SYLVIE: Don't worry, you'll see her all right. But you must be quiet, Peter.

PETER FROST: [*Jeeringly*] Haw-haw!

SOUND: *Howling of Catherine-the-cat from attic.*

PETER FROST: Well, what are we waiting for? I want to see your old ghost.

SYLVIE:
JANE:
⎫
⎬ [*Together in solemn voices*] Very well, then.
JOE: ⎭   Follow us.
RUFUS:

SOUND: *Footsteps going upstairs.*

JOE: Now we go up the stepladder. I'll push open the hatch.

PETER FROST: Why don't you light your flash, Joe?

JOE: And scare away the ghost, I suppose? You know a ghost isn't comin' out where there's a light and so many people. That is, unless there's a certain person around it happens to be interested in.

SOUND: *Howling of cat.*

JOE: There, I've pushed the trap-door up with my shoulder.

SOUND: *Groaning of trap-door as it gives. Thud of children as they hoist themselves up.*

194

Joe: Now that we're all up, I'll flash my light into the corners. Gee, there's a stuffed wildcat. Look over there at Madame-the-ghost. She's coming toward us.

Jane: Peter Frost! Peter Frost! E-e-e-e-e-e-e-e-e-e-e!

Sound: *Noise of the dress form being pushed about by chains. Howling of cat.*

Peter Frost: Oh! Gee! She's after me! Let me go! Let me out of here!

Sound: *Running, stumbling, falling, screaming—then running down stairs.*

Peter Frost: [*From downstairs*] She's got me! She's got me!

Rufus: [*Screaming*] Mama! Mama!

Jane: Oh, the flashlight's gone out. Let's get out of here.

Joe: Phew! Some ghost, I'll say.

Rufus: 'Twas real, then?

Joe: Of course not, silly. Come on, though. We've got to get the things down. Mama'll be home in a minute. Sylvie, you'd better carry the little lamp. Then you'd better dress Madame in Mrs. Shoemaker's new dress and put her in the Grape Room.

Music: *Bridge.*

Jane: Gee, wasn't Peter Frost scared! That'll teach him to be always tormentin' the life outa us.

Sylvie: Sh-h-h! Here comes Mama.

Sound: *Door opening and closing.*

MAMA: Goodness, the witches certainly must be out tonight all right. I just passed Peter Frost racing like sixty up the street and he was muttering some gibberish about a ghost being after him. And look at Catherine-the-cat! She looks as though she's preparing for a wild night. And why, for goodness sake! Just look here! Mrs. Shoemaker's dress is turned completely around. The hobgoblins must have done it. Well, well!

RUFUS: [*Smothering his laughter*] Come on, let's bob for apples.

The Tinker and the Ghost

From the book, *The Three Golden Oranges*, by Ralph Steele
Boggs and Mary Gould Davis. Published by Longmans, Green &
Company. Reproduced by permission of the publishers. Adapted for
radio by Katherine Watson. (Grades 5-6) 5 minutes

CAST OF CHARACTERS

ESTEBAN ....,............................... tinker
WIVES
GHOST
VOICES

SOUNDS

Fire crackling
Thump
Breaking of egg
Sizzling of bacon

Footsteps
Digging
Howling of wind
Music

The Tinker and the Ghost

ANNOUNCER: On the wide plain not far from the city of Toledo, there stood a great gray castle. For many years no one dwelt there, because the castle was haunted. Every night of the year a thin, sad voice moaned and wailed through the empty rooms. And on All Hallow's Eve a ghostly light appeared in the chimney and flared against the dark sky. Many who had tried to exorcise the ghost were found dead the next morning. Now one day in October, there came to the village a brave and jolly tinker whose name was Esteban. While he sat in the market place mending the pans of the wives, he heard about the haunted castle. We hear him talking to the women, who didn't think he'd dare go near the castle.

ESTEBAN: If I dare! You must know that I, Esteban, fear nothing, neither ghost nor human. I will gladly sleep in the castle tonight and keep this dismal spirit company. I certainly will be glad to get the thousand gold coins as a reward. I'll just go to the castle tonight and try to get rid of this thing that haunts it. But you must bring me a load of faggots, a slice of bacon, a flask of wine, a dozen fresh eggs, and a frying pan.

WIVES: [*Together*] We will, we will.

ANNOUNCER: It was a dark night. Esteban unsaddled his donkey and set him to graze on the short grass. Then he carried his food and his faggots into the great hall. After he had a fire, he settled himself comfortably on the hearth.

SOUND: *Fire crackling. Howling of wind.*

ESTEBAN: That fire is certainly the thing to keep off both cold and fear. I'll just have some of this bacon. Oh! How good it smells!

SOUND: *Sizzling of bacon.*

GHOST: [*From chimney*] Oh, me! Oh, me!

ESTEBAN: Not a very cheerful greeting, my friend, but bearable to a man who is used to the braying of his donkey.

GHOST: Oh, me! Oh, me!

SOUND: *Breaking of egg into pan.*

GHOST: Look out below! I'm falling!

ESTEBAN: All right. Only don't fall into the frying pan.

SOUND: *Thump.*

ESTEBAN: Oh! my goodness! A man's leg. And clothed in a pair of brown corduroy trousers. Oh! This egg is good, and this wine is delicious. I wish, though, the wind wouldn't howl so much around this castle.

GHOST: Look out below! I'm falling!

SOUND: *Thump.*

ESTEBAN: Well, if it isn't a second leg, just like the first! I think I'll have another egg.

GHOST: Look out below. I'm falling!

ESTEBAN: Fall away. Only don't spill my egg.

SOUND: *Thump.*

ESTEBAN: My goodness! A man's trunk clothed in a blue shirt and a brown corduroy coat.

SOUND: *Thump.*

ESTEBAN: Oh! there are two arms. Now there is only the head left to fall down. I confess that I am rather curious to see that.

GHOST: Look out below! I'm falling—falling.

SOUND: *Heavy thump.*

ESTEBAN: Well, if it isn't the head! It has thick black hair, a long black beard, and dark eyes that look worried. Why, do my eyes deceive me? The parts of the body have joined together. Good evening! Are you man or ghost? Will you have an egg and a bit of bacon?

GHOST: No, I want no food. But I will tell you this right here and now—you are the only man out of all those who have come to the castle to stay here until I could get my body together again. The others died of sheer fright before I was half finished.

ESTEBAN: That is because they did not have sense enough to bring food and fire with them.

GHOST: If you will help me a bit more, you will save my soul and get me into the Kingdom of Heaven. Out in the courtyard, under a cypress tree, there are buried three bags—one of copper coins, one of silver coins, and one of gold coins. But no sooner did I have them buried than the thieves overtook me, murdered me, and cut my body into pieces. But they did not find the coins. Now you come with me and dig them up. Give the copper coins to the church, the silver coins to the poor, and keep the gold coins for yourself. Then I will have expiated my sins and can go to the Kingdom of Heaven.

200

ESTEBAN: That's fine with me. I'll go out into the courtyard with you.

SOUND: *Footsteps.*

GHOST: Now dig!

ESTEBAN: Dig yourself!

SOUND: *Digging.*

GHOST: Well, here are the three bags. Now will you
promise to do just what I ask you to do?

ESTEBAN: Yes, I promise.

GHOST: Then strip my garments from me.

ESTEBAN: All right, if you want me to do that. [*Pause*]
What else? Where have you gone? My goodness,
where are you? Well, anyway, I have the coins. I'll
just fry another egg and then go to sleep.

MUSIC: *Musical curtain.*

ANNOUNCER: The next morning when the village people
came to carry Esteban's body away, they found him
making an omelette out of the last of the fresh eggs.
We hear—

VOICES: Gracious! Are you alive?

ESTEBAN: I am indeed. The food and faggots lasted
through the night very nicely. Now I will go to the
owner of the castle and collect my thousand gold coins.
The ghost has gone for good and all. You will find
his clothes lying out in the courtyard. Now I must be
going, for I have to collect my money from the lord of
the castle. Then I'll return to Toledo and give the
copper coins to the curate of my church and distribute
the silver ones among the poor. Good-by.

VOICES: And may you live in contentment all your years.

Becky's Thanksgiving Turkey

From the book, *Becky Landers; Frontier Warrior,* by Constance Lindsay Skinner. Published by the Macmillan Company. Reproduced by permission of the publishers. Adapted for radio by Katherine Watson. (Grades 5-6)   7 minutes

CAST OF CHARACTERS

BECKY LANDERS .... a pioneer girl of fifteen
MOTHER ....Becky's mother
GEORGE ROGERS CLARK .... a frontiersman
1ST MAN .... a member of Clark's expedition
2ND MAN (JEFF) .... a member of Clark's expedition

SOUNDS

Gun shots   Footsteps
Shouts   Indian yells
Door opening   Water
Door closing

Becky's Thanksgiving Turkey

ANNOUNCER: Becky Landers, being the man of the family, knew that if there was to be turkey for the Thanksgiving dinner, she would have to provide it. Since the younger members of the household—Ted, aged seven and Ruth, aged four and a half, had decreed turkey, the point was already settled. Their mother said that it would be nice to give them what they wanted at Thanksgiving because there was so little to give children in Kentucky, except peril. Ever since the Indians had killed her husband and captured her eldest son, Rod, Mrs. Landers had been very sad. We now hear Becky say—

BECKY: Mother, we well know how the Indians love strength and courage. Those who came here as friends always admired Rod because he was so tall and straight, and could run, jump, shoot, and wrestle as well as any of their own boys. The Indians didn't kill Rod, Mother —I know they didn't. I just know it. Now, I must be starting out to find our Thanksgiving turkey.

MOTHER: Becky, don't go too far.

BECKY: Don't worry, Mother. Good-by.

SOUND: *Door opening and closing.*

BECKY: [*To herself*] It's quite a responsibility being the man of the family. I can hunt, yes, but I can't fight. How I wish I could go with George Rogers Clark and his men when they make their raid on Kaskaskia and find Rod! Clark said that if Virginia would only send him the powder and lead, he'd take two hundred and fifty men and rush down on Kaskaskia and Vincennes, and capture them before the enemy knew they were there. I think he is brave and very handsome.

ANNOUNCER: Becky had walked rapidly for two hours and had long ago left the fort far behind. She knew that there was comparatively little danger of a raid in winter. Summer was the Indians' war season. But, just the same, she kept a careful lookout for signs of Indians. Suddenly, both human beings and turkeys appeared at once. On the river, she espied a large boat. It was heading for the shore directly in front of her, and it was a white man's boat. Becky was about to run across the fifty yards of open space to the landing-place when she caught sight of turkey feathers. We now hear her counting their tails.

BECKY: Oh! My Thanksgiving dinner! One turkey, two, three, four—more still, a flock of a dozen, perhaps eighteen. I must hurry before the boatmen get to shore and startle the whole flock.

SOUND: *Firing of gun. Shots and shouts from men in boat. Indian yells.*

BECKY: Oh, my goodness! My turkeys are Redskins in ambush! I must reload quickly and warn the men in the boat.

SOUND: *A single shot and then a volley.*

BECKY: Thank goodness! There they go.

LEADER: [*From boat*] Hullo-oo there. Come on out, you fellows, and let's shake hands with you.

SOUND: *Water.*

BECKY: Hullo.

204

LEADER: A girl! A girl, by thunder!

1ST MAN: Three cheers for the girl. Why, it's Becky Landers.

BECKY: Why, I remember you two men, Bill Canty and Jeff Smoke, as ruffians from Maybrook. [*To leader*] Are you a highwayman, too?

LEADER: Sort of—

BECKY: Because if you are, I haven't anything but my rifle, and we need that so terribly. You see, I have to take care of Mother and the children.

1ST MAN: That's right. Becky's the man o' the family ever since the Injuns ran off with her brother.

LEADER: Becky Landers, you're a first-class fighting man and we're proud to know you. Maybe you've heard of me. My name's Clark.

BECKY: [*Gasps*] Not George Rogers Clark!

CLARK: That's me, Becky.

BECKY: But, you said you were a highwayman!

CLARK: Well, that's the mildest name they're calling me back in Virginia right now. You see, I've got a boat-load of powder down the river. The Virginia Assembly wouldn't vote it to me because they said they couldn't afford it. So I told them if they didn't, I'd raise three or four hundred men out here and take Kentucky for myself.

2ND MAN: We could do it, too, b'gosh.!

CLARK: For I said if they thought Kentucky is not worth defending, they can't think it worth holding; so it'll be no loss to them. They were afraid I meant it. So, —they gave me the powder. But the Governor said I was no better than a highwayman. Now you see why I answered "sort of" when you asked me.

BECKY: I see.

CLARK: And, Becky, if these Indians had killed me and my friends here and had captured the powder, it's likely the British would have taken Kentucky. That powder's going along in our powder horns, Becky, to Kaskaskia and Vincennes. When you shot at those savages, just now, Becky Landers, maybe you fired the shot that'll save Kentucky.

BECKY: I didn't fire at savages. I don't deserve your praise, for I only saw their tails—I mean—I thought they were turkeys and I promised the babies a Thanksgiving turkey.

CLARK: Jeff, run down to the boat and fetch the two turkeys I shot this morning.

2ND MAN: Right away.

SOUND: *Footsteps.*

CLARK: You boys can eat deer. And you'd better fall to as soon as you've pitched camp. I'll sleep at Kenton's tonight. But first, I'm going home with Becky Landers and her Thanksgiving turkeys. I want to tell Mrs. Landers that her daughter is a great soldier. You needn't blush, Becky, even if you did shoot just because you thought they were turkeys, you kept on even after you knew they were Indians. It took brains to know that was the best thing to do, and it took courage to do it. When we eat dinner in Kaskaskia, boys, we'll drink the first toast to Becky Landers, the lass who saved our powder.

ALL THE MEN: You bet we will.

The Pumpkin Giant

From *Pot of Gold,* by Mary E. (Wilkins) Freeman. Published by Lothrop, Lee & Shepard Co. Reproduced by permission of the publishers. Adapted for radio by Katherine Watson. (Grades 3-4)

10 minutes

CAST OF CHARACTERS

KING

PRIME MINISTER

PATROCLUS

AENEAS ....,,..... son of Patroclus

DAPHNE ....,...... wife of Patroclus

PAGE

SOUNDS

Door opening and closing
Choking and gasping of giant
Music
Rumbling

Footsteps
Weeping
Throwing of potato

The Pumpkin Giant

ANNOUNCER: A very long time ago, before our grandmother's time, or our great-grandmother's, there were no pumpkins. People had never eaten a pumpkin pie; and that was the time when the Pumpkin Giant flourished. This giant was an uncommonly bad one. Let's listen in to the King of the country who is talking to the Prime Minister—

KING: Something has to be done about this Pumpkin Giant. My people are all becoming so frightened they have what is known as the Giant's Shakes. And you should see this terrible giant. His eyes are big and round, and glow like coals of fire. His mouth, which stretches half around his head, is full of rows of pointed teeth, and he always holds it wide open.

PRIME MINISTER: Where does he live?

KING: He lives in a castle situated on a mountain, with the usual courtyard before it, and imagine, the moat is full of—bones.

PRIME MINISTER: But I don't understand. Why is that?

KING: Well, you see the Pumpkin Giant is fonder of little girls and boys than anything else in the world, and especially of *fat* little boys. If something isn't done about it there may be very few fat little girls and no fat little boys left in the kingdom. And what makes matters worse, it is known that the Giant has commenced taking a tonic to increase his appetite. The reason I'm so frightened is because of my only daughter, the Princess Ariadne Diana, for you know she is *fat*. She is considered the fattest princess in the whole world. The Princess has never walked a step in the dozen years of her life, but just has to roll, and is never allowed to leave the palace without a bodyguard of fifty knights.

PRIME MINISTER: But what is to be done?

KING: I have issued a proclamation that I will knight anyone, be he noble or common, who will cut off the head of the Pumpkin Giant.

ANNOUNCER: There was one man who lived not far from the terrible Giant's castle. His name was Patroclus and his wife's name was Daphne. He was very poor and had a boy, Aeneas, twelve years old, who was almost as fat as the Princess. Patroclus, the father, made his living from his potato field. Let's listen in to their conversation while they are out digging potatoes.

PATROCLUS: My son, I think we've dug perhaps a bushel of these Young Plantagenet potatoes. How large they are! Oh! My goodness, the earth is trembling. It's the Pumpkin Giant coming. Get behind me, my son!

SOUND: *Rumbling.*

PATROCLUS: Don't be afraid, Aeneas. I'll throw one of these huge potatoes at him as soon as he comes nearer. Oh! He's coming faster and faster. Now I'll throw it.

SOUND: *Throwing of potato.*

PATROCLUS: There, I've hit him in the mouth.

SOUND: *Choking and gasping of giant.*

209

Patroclus: Oooh! Hurrah! I think I've killed the Pumpkin Giant. Sure enough—he's dead. We won't be bothered with him any more. I'll just chop off his head.

Aeneas: Oh, Father, may I have the Giant's head to play with? The boys will all envy me.

Music: *Musical curtain.*

Announcer: The king was notified of the death of the Pumpkin Giant, but though his gratitude for the noble deed knew no bounds, he omitted to give the promised reward and knight Patroclus. Aeneas was proud of his possession of the Giant's head, but he played so much with it that it got broken and the seeds were scattered all over the field. Next spring all over Patroclus' potato field grew running vines, and in the fall Giant's heads. There they were all over the field, hundreds of them. People were afraid that since there was one Pumpkin Giant before, now there would be a whole army of them. If it was dreadful then, what would it be in the future? Aeneas had a habit of putting everything into his mouth and tasting it and we hear him say—

Aeneas: I wonder how a Giant's head would taste? I think I'll take a bite. If I get sick I know Mother will give me an antidote, as she has done so many times before. Oh! This is good, so nice and sweet. I think I'd better go in and tell her what I've eaten, and take an antidote.

Sound: *Footsteps. Door opens and closes.*

Aeneas: Mother, I've eaten two thirds of a Giant's head and I guess you had better give me an antidote.

DAPHNE: Oh, my precious son, how could you? There is no antidote in my book for a Giant's head. What shall we do? I just know you'll die.

SOUND: *Weeping of both mother and son.*

AENEAS: It's strange but I've never felt so well in all my life. [*Laughs*] I'm not going to die, Mother. I feel wonderful. Please stop crying! And now I'm going to get some more of that Giant's head. I'm hungry.

DAPHNE: Don't, don't! It might be poisonous.

SOUND: *Footsteps fading out.*

MUSIC: *Musical curtain.*

AENEAS: See here, father and mother, I have a whole Giant's head. Do have some of this—it is so good. A great deal better than potatoes. Please taste it, Mother!

DAPHNE: It is good, but I think it would be better cooked. We must gather all the Giant's heads and store them in the cellar, and I will bake pies every day.

ANNOUNCER: One morning the King had been out hunting and happened to ride by the cottage of Patroclus with a train of his knights. His wife was baking pies as usual and as both window and door were open, the delicious odor of the pies filled the air. We hear the King say—

KING: What is it smells so utterly lovely? Page, you run into the cottage and find out.

SOUND: *Footsteps.*

PAGE: Your Majesty, the housewife is baking Giant's head pies. That's what smells so delicious.

211

KING: [*Thunders*] What! Bring one out to me!

SOUND: *Footsteps.*

PAGE: Here you are, Your Majesty!

KING: I never tasted anything so altogether superfine, so utterly magnificent, in all my life. Stewed peacock's tongues from the Baltic are not to be compared with it! Call out the housewife immediately.

SOUND: *Footsteps of Daphne, Patroclus and Aeneas.*

DAPHNE: [*Trembling*] Did you wish to see me, Your Highness?

KING: Yes, I sent for you to ask about those delicious pies. I will reward you as becomes a monarch.

DAPHNE: My husband can tell you about the Giant's heads better than I.

PATROCLUS: I'll tell you the whole story from the very beginning. You remember Your Majesty's promise to knight anyone who— [*Fading out into musical bridge*]

KING: I did forget to knight you, oh, noble and brave man! And to make a lady of your admirable wife! So I will knight you now, with my bejeweled sword.

MUSIC: *Musical curtain.*

ANNOUNCER: The whole family went to live at the royal palace. The roses in the royal garden were uprooted, and the Giant's heads (or pumpkins, as they came to be called) were sown in their stead; all the royal parks also were turned into pumpkin fields. Patroclus was in constant attendance on the King, while Daphne superintended the baking of the pumpkin pies, and Aeneas finally married the Princess Ariadne Diana and they lived happily ever after.

Animals

Justin Morgan Had a Horse

From *Justin Morgan Had a Horse,* by Marguerite Henry. Published by Wilcox & Follett Co. Reproduced by permission of the publishers. Adapted for radio by Katherine Watson. (Grades 5-6)
15 minutes

CAST OF CHARACTERS

JUSTIN MORGAN .... school teacher
JOEL GOSS .... young friend of Morgan
ABNER BEANE .... a farmer
MILLER CHASE .... inn keeper and sawmill owner
EVANS .... hired man
NATHAN NYE .... neighbor
TIMOTHY TUBBS .... Joel's friend
TEAMSTER ⎫
1ST MAN ⎬ .... bystanders
2ND MAN ⎭

SOUNDS

Cheers

Footsteps

Neighing of horse

Whimper of horse

Justin Morgan had a Horse

ANNOUNCER: This is the story of a common, ordinary little work horse that turned out to be the father of a famous family of American horses. He lived in the Green Mountain country of Vermont in the days when our country was growing up. Justin Morgan, the schoolmaster, and Joel Goss are on their way from Randolph, Vermont to Springfield, Massachusetts, to collect a bad debt. We hear Justin talking to Joel after their long trip.

JUSTIN: We're here, Joel. We can put our bundles down and rest a spell before we go in.

JOEL: [*Not hearing*] Look at the little horse. I could gentle him, I could.

JUSTIN: Halloo there, Abner Beane.

ABNER BEANE: Morning! Great Jumping Jehoshaphat! If it ain't Justin Morgan, schoolmaster and singing teacher. Why, I'm as pleasured to see you as a dog with two tails. And who's the young feller here?

JUSTIN: This young lad is my friend, Joel Goss. I boarded with his parents last school year. Joel, I want you to meet an old friend.

ABNER BEANE: Where in tarnation you two come from? You haven't come all the ways from Randolph, Vermont to Springfield, Massachusetts!

JUSTIN: Yep, we have.

ABNER BEANE: Sakes alive! You must be all tuckered out. Why, it's over a hundred miles down here. Didn't walk the whole way, I hope?

JUSTIN: No, Abner, we came part way with Lem Tubbs and his team of oxen.

ABNER BEANE: Well, let's not stand here a-gabbing. Come in. Come in. The woman'll give us some hot johnny-cake and coffee.

JUSTIN: Before Joel and I eat your victuals, it seems as though I should tell you I've come to collect the money you owed me when I moved away to Vermont.

ABNER BEANE: You have come a terrible long way, Justin, and 'tis hard for me to disappoint you. But me and the woman have had nothing but trouble. I just hain't got the money.

JUSTIN: I'd set much store on getting it.

ABNER BEANE: But I ain't one to forget my debts. I've a mind to give you a colt instead of the cash. Now this big feller, this Ebenezer, is a creature with get-up-and-get. He'll be a go-ahead horse. It would be hard to find a more sensibler animal if you looked all up and down the Connecticut Valley. Besides, he's halter-broke. He's just the horse to ride to school.

JUSTIN: It would be just another mouth to feed.

ABNER BEANE: [*Laughs*] Why, bless my breeches, I bet you could sell him before you run up a feed bill. All the river folk got their eyes on him. He'll fetch a pocket of money. Maybe twice as much as I owe you.

JUSTIN: I don't know what to say.

ABNER BEANE: And now for the premium! I'll give you Little Bub, here, too. 'Course he ain't the colt that Ebenezer is. He's just a little mite of a thing. But there's something about those two. They stay together as snug as two peas in a pod. Scarcely ever do you see one of the creatures alone. Eb's kind of a mother to Bub. You'd actually think the colt was his.

217

Justin: I don't need two horses any more than I need water in my hat. It would be just two more mouths to feed.

Joel: [*Timidly*] Reckon I could feed them, Master Morgan?

Justin: In the hills of Vermont, lad, farmers want big handsome oxen, not undersized horses.

Abner Beane: Look ahere, Justin, at Ebenezer's feet! You know the good from the bad. Bub's only pint size, but he's got a good disposition. Except when he sees a dog. He just can't abide dogs. They make him mad as a hornet.

Justin: It's kind of you to offer both colts, Abner, but you keep Little Bub. In Vermont I can sell Ebenezer, but the little creature would just be a worry to me.

Announcer: It is now the next morning. Ebenezer and Little Bub are turned out to pasture. Joel goes up to the horses with an apple in his hand. After quite a few minutes, the colt takes it and we hear Joel talking to Little Bub—

Joel: Oh! I wish you were mine. Ebenezer's big and fine, but you and me—we could grow big together. [*Calling*] I'm here, Master Morgan. Are you looking for me?

Justin: Yes, we must be on our way. I'm grateful to you, Abner, for Ebenezer. Maybe he'll be worth his salt after all.

Abner Beane: And I'm obliged to you for crossing off the debt, Justin. 'Twas extraordinary nice of you to put it in writing. I always did say you was the handsomest writer and the best singer in the whole state of Massachusetts.

Justin: Good-by, Abner.

ABNER BEANE: Hey, Justin! The little one is coming along, too.

JOEL: [*Whispering*] Please God, don't let Little Bub turn back! Please God, don't let him turn back!

ANNOUNCER: To Joel's great joy, Little Bub did follow them all the way back to Vermont. Nobody but the boy, Joel, set much store by Little Bub; but as the years went by, the colt grew into a courageous little work horse. Worry struck at Joel's heart for fear Justin Morgan would sell Little Bub. Joel became an apprentice to Miller Chase, the keeper of the village inn, and owner of a sawmill. The night before he was sent to live with him, Justin Morgan called Joel to his room and we hear—

JUSTIN: Two good things happened to me today. The Jenks family have agreed to board me, and I've found an honest horse dealer.

JOEL: But the little colt—he's not sold?

JUSTIN: I've a good home for Ebenezer; but everywhere I try to sell Little Bub, the answer is the same. Too small! Too small! And, besides, they say—the creature isn't even broken to saddle or harness! Now, what I ask of you is this, Joel—

JOEL: Yes?

JUSTIN: Do you think you could gentle Little Bub?

JOEL: After watching Pa do it ever since I was a baby? Course I could! But you mean I'm to gentle him—for someone else?

JUSTIN: That's what I mean, lad. We are both fonder of Little Bub than men should be of any beast, but I have debts to pay, and I must pay them before I die. I need your help, Joel. Will you shake hands, man to man?

219

JOEL: Yes.

JUSTIN: I've been to see Miller Chase, and he plans to send you to night school. I wonder if you would like to spend an hour with the colt each night after lessons?

JOEL: In the dark?

JUSTIN: There's a moon. For two weeks there will be light enough for you to see. Horses, you know, can see quite well in the dark.

ANNOUNCER: And so Joel trained Little Bub. For months the schoolmaster said no more about selling the colt; and then Ezra Fisk, a new settler, rented Little Bub for fifteen dollars a year and his keep. One afternoon, early in May, Joel stood looking out of the inn door. Suddenly the yard began filling with big-faced dray horses and oxen, and men were gathering about a huge pine log. Into the yard came Ezra's hired man, Evans, riding Little Bub. We hear him saying—

EVANS: Hey, what's all the hullabaloo, Nathan Nye?

NATHAN NYE: 'Tis a pulling bee, but none of the beasts can pull that there pine log to the sawmill in three pulls or less. Even Wiggin's beast failed. None of them can budge the log.

EVANS: None except my one-horse team.

NATHAN NYE: That little flea? Why, he's just a sample of a horse.

EVANS: He ain't exactly what you'd call a dray horse, but whatever he's hitched to generally has to come the first time trying.

NATHAN NYE: Take him on home. When we have a contest for ponies, we'll be letting you know.

SOUND: *Footsteps receding.*

EVANS: Chase, I'll wager a barrel of cider that my horse can move that pine log to the sawmill in two pulls.

JOEL: Mister Evans, Little Bub's been dragging logs all day. You hain't going to enter him in the pulling bee?

EVANS: Go away, Joel. When I want advice, I'll not ask it of a whippersnapper. Come out and see.

SOUND: *Footsteps approaching.*

NATHAN NYE: Want to give up before you start, Evans?

EVANS: No such thing. Why, I'm actually ashamed to ask my horse to pull such a little log. Now if you'll find me three stout men to sit astride the log, why then I'll ask him. Look to your feet, men! This horse means business. Something's got to give. [*Roars*] Git up!

ANNOUNCER: The little horse galvanized into action. His powerful neck bent low. Now he was straining forward. You could see his muscles grow firm and swell up like rubber balls. At last the log trembled and moved. This time it did not stop until it reached the sawmill. Let's listen in to the crowd!

SOUND: *Cheers.*

CROWD: Hooray for Morgan's colt! Hooray! Hooray! Hooray for the big-little horse!

JOEL: It's over! It's over! You did it, Little Bub! You did it!

ANNOUNCER: Yes, Little Bub did pull the log. Everyone was amazed at the strength of the little horse. Several months later Justin Morgan and Joel were walking the half mile into Randolph. When almost there, the schoolmaster put out his hand and tucked five silver dollars into Joel's. We hear Joel say—

221

JOEL: Do you know, I reckon now I can buy Little Bub when I'm of age. Miller Chase has promised to give me two suits of clothes then, but I aim to ask for the money instead. And with these five dollars besides, why, I'll be able to buy Little Bub as easy as anything.

JUSTIN: He'll be very old then, lad, and you'll be man-grown.

JOEL: Things are working out fine, Master Morgan.

JUSTIN: Things are working out fine for me, too, Joel. I can pay my debts now—to the very last dollar.

ANNOUNCER: By autumn Little Bub's year of rental was up, and he was returned to Justin Morgan who left for Woodstock, Vermont, taking the horse with him. Then a letter came to Joel from Justin Morgan telling him that he was once again in debt and that he was leaving Little Bub to the family who had taken care of him during his illness. He added that he knew sometime Joel would find a way to take care of their horse. Then soon afterward, Justin Morgan died and his name was given to Little Bub. Joel's years of apprenticeship were almost over. Then an unbelievable thing happened. Justin Morgan was sold to a traveler and dropped out of sight. After many cruel years of separation, Joel on his way to a meeting, stopped to pick up a friend, Timothy Tubbs.

SOUND: *Neighing of horse.*

JOEL: So help me, Timothy—seems as though I've heard that particular neigh before. It comes from the direction of Chase's Inn.

TIMOTHY: Likely you have.

JOEL: Come on, I'm going to find him. We'll look in the shed first.

222

SOUND: *Footsteps.*

JOEL: No, he isn't here. But there——

SOUND: *Neighing of horse.*

JOEL: There it is again. He must be in front of the inn. Oh! there is a team of six horses hitched to a freight wagon.

SOUND: *Neighing of horse.*

JOEL: So help me! 'Tis the littlest horse in the team. 'Tis Justin Morgan! That's who 'tis—Justin Morgan! Oh! My poor Little Bub—my poor, shivering, frightened Little Bub oh—you are so thin.

SOUND: *Whimper of horse.*

JOEL: Timothy, it hain't going to be easy to make you understand about this little horse. But when I knew him he could walk faster, run faster, and pull heavier logs than any other horse in Vermont! 'Tis the Justin Morgan horse, Timothy! 'Tis the Justin Morgan horse, I tell you!

TIMOTHY: This old beast the singing master's horse?

JOEL: The very one. Let's find the owner. He may be in Chase's Inn.

SOUND: *Footsteps.*

JOEL: Gentlemen! Who owns the six-horse team at the hitching block?

TEAMSTER: [*Snarling*] I do! And what's it to you?

JOEL: How much do you want for the littlest horse in your team?

TEAMSTER: Young feller, I wouldn't hear of selling him nowise. That little horse can pull better than all the clodhoppers in the team put together. Why, 'twas less than a fortnight ago I turned down twenty dollars for him!

JOEL: Mr. Chase, ever since I was a little tyke, I've hankered for the Morgan horse. Now he's right here in the innyard—and if I don't buy him tonight, sir, he may be dead in the morning.

CHASE: Joel, lad, you have your own sawmill now, and you may be an old man by the time it is paid for. Times are awful hard. What's the sense of getting in debt on a nearly dead beast? The Morgan horse must be in his twenties, and any horse that old is liable to be rheumaticky and die soon.

JOEL: Yes, yes, I know. But this horse is different, sir. He's a friend, and you don't turn down a friend just because he's old.

CHASE: All right, son. I'll lend you whatever it takes.

ANNOUNCER: And so Joel bought Little Bub. No human patient ever received more tender care than did the little horse. It was like magic the way Justin Morgan responded. His body grew round. His eyes became lively and lustrous again. One fine July morning— July 24th, 1817—we hear Joel talking to his beloved horse—

JOEL: Listen, Justin, in an hour you and I are going to be in a parade, and the President of the United States will be there. Do you know, you're just naturally growing young. Your heart be young and so be you. I bet there hain't a finer horse in all the nineteen states.

ANNOUNCER: An hour later Joel and his horse were swing-
ing into formation. There were many different kinds
of horses. But to Joel, none had the gallant spirit of
Justin Morgan. How happy he was to have the little
horse for his own! And then a deep voice boomed,
"Ladies and Gentlemen, the President of the United
States." Then James Monroe himself was escorted between the rows of men mounted on horseback. When
he came to Justin Morgan, he stopped and motioned to
have him brought forward out of line. The little horse
seemed to understand the greatness of the occasion.
He allowed the President to mount with ease. When
the parade reached College Hill, the President dis-
mounted and made a speech. He said that no nation
had a richer treasure than liberty. The crowds went
wild. It was hard to tell whether the President of the
United States or the little horse was the hero of the
day. We hear one man in the crowd—

1ST MAN: I always knew he would be a go-ahead horse.

2ND MAN: And I can remember when schoolmaster Morgan couldn't sell the creature nohow. And here he's
outlived two horses!

1ST MAN: Fellers, I more than half believe the Morgan
horse is human.

JOEL: Why, come to think of it, he's like us. He's American, that's what he is. American!

ANNOUNCER: And now for a tribute to Justin Morgan.
In the tiny Vermont village of Weybridge, the United
States Department of Agriculture has a Morgan Horse
Farm. In all America it is the only farm founded so
that one breed of horses shall live forever.
    At the entrance gate to the farm stands a life-size
bronze statue of Justin Morgan. Proud history lives
in the simple inscription: the history of a common,

ordinary little work horse that turned out to be the father of a great breed of American horses; the history of a gallant little horse that blazed a trail in the wilderness and helped build a new nation; the history of Justin Morgan, pioneer American.

Humor

The Peterkins Too Late for Amanda's School-Exhibition in Boston

By Lucretia P. Hale from the *St. Nicholas Magazine*, October 1875. Published by D. Appleton-Century Company. Reproduced by permission of the publishers. Adapted for radio by Katherine Watson. (Grades 5-6) 8 minutes

CAST OF CHARACTERS

AMANDA .... friend of Elizabeth Eliza
MOTHER .... Amanda's mother
MRS. PETERKIN
ELIZABETH ELIZA .... Mrs. Peterkin's daughter
JULIA .... friend

SOUNDS

Voices   Footsteps
Door closing

The Peterkins Too Late for Amanda's School-Exhibition in Boston

SOUND: *Door closing—many footsteps.*

AMANDA: Mother, the exhibition is over, and I have brought the whole class home to the collation.

MOTHER: The whole class! But I expected only a few.

AMANDA: The rest are coming. I brought Julie and Clara and Sophie with me.

SOUND: *Voices and footsteps of two people.*

AMANDA: Here are the rest.

MOTHER: Why, no. It is Mrs. Peterkin and Elizabeth Eliza!

AMANDA: Too late for the exhibition. Such a shame! But in time for the collation.

MOTHER: [*To herself*] If the ice-cream will go round.

AMANDA: But what made you so late? Did you miss the train? This is Elizabeth Eliza, girls. You have heard me speak of her. What a pity you were too late!

MRS. PETERKIN: We tried to come—we did our best.

MOTHER: Did you miss the train? Didn't you get my postal-card?

MRS. PETERKIN: We had nothing to do with the train.

AMANDA: You don't mean you walked?

Mrs. Peterkin: Oh no, indeed!

Elizabeth Eliza: We came in a horse and carry-all.

Julia: I always wondered how anybody could come in a horse!

Amanda: You are too foolish, Julia. They came in the carry-all part. But didn't you start in time?

Mrs. Peterkin: It all comes from the carry-all being so hard to turn. I told Mr. Peterkin we should get into trouble with one of those carry-alls that don't turn easy.

Elizabeth Eliza: They turn easy enough in the stable, so you can't tell.

Mrs. Peterkin: Yes, we started with the little boys and Solomon John on the back seat, and Elizabeth Eliza on the front. She was to drive, and I was to see to the driving. But the horse was not faced toward Boston.

Mother: And you tipped over in turning round! Oh, what an accident!

Amanda: And the little boys—where are they? Are they killed?

Elizabeth Eliza: The little boys are all safe. We left them at the Pringles', with Solomon John.

Mother: But what did happen?

Mrs. Peterkin: We started the wrong way.

Mother: You lost your way, after all?

Elizabeth Eliza: No; we knew the way well enough.

Amanda: It's as plain as a pike-staff!

Mrs. Peterkin: No; we had the horse faced in the wrong direction, toward Providence.

ELIZABETH ELIZA: And mother was afraid to have me turn, and we kept on and on till we should reach a wide place.

MRS. PETERKIN: I thought we should come to a road that would veer off to the right or left and bring us back to the right direction.

MOTHER: Could you not all get out and turn the thing round?

MRS. PETERKIN: Why, no. If it had broken down we should not have been in anything, and could not have gone anywhere.

ELIZABETH ELIZA: Yes, I have always heard it was best to stay in the carriage whatever happens.

JULIA: But nothing seemed to happen.

MRS. PETERKIN: Oh, yes, we met one man after another, and we asked the way to Boston.

ELIZABETH ELIZA: And all they would say was, "Turn right round—you are on the road to Providence."

MRS. PETERKIN: As if we could turn right round! That was just what we couldn't.

MOTHER: You don't mean you kept on all the way to Providence?

ELIZABETH ELIZA: Oh dear, no! We kept on and on, till we met a man with a black handbag—black leather I should say.

JULIA: He must have been a book-agent.

MRS. PETERKIN: I dare say he was; his bag seemed heavy. He set it on a stone.

MOTHER: I dare say it was the same one that came here the other day. He wanted me to buy the "History of the Aborigines, Brought Up From Earliest Times to the Present Date," in four volumes. I told him I hadn't time to read so much. He said that was no matter, few did, and it wasn't much worth it—they bought books for the look of the thing.

AMANDA: Now, that was illiterate; he could never have graduated. I hope, Elizabeth Eliza, you had nothing to do with that man.

ELIZABETH ELIZA: Very likely it was not the same man.

MOTHER: Did he have a kind of pepper-and-salt suit, with one of the buttons worn?

MRS. PETERKIN: I noticed one of the buttons was off.

AMANDA: We're off the subject. Did you buy his book?

ELIZABETH ELIZA: He never offered us his book.

MRS. PETERKIN: He told us the same story—we were going to Providence; if we wanted to go to Boston, we must turn directly round.

ELIZABETH ELIZA: I told him I couldn't; but he took the horse's head, and the first thing I knew—

AMANDA: He had yanked you round!

MRS. PETERKIN: I screamed; I couldn't help it!

ELIZABETH ELIZA: I was glad when it was over!

MOTHER: Well, well, it shows the disadvantage of starting wrong.

MRS. PETERKIN: Yes, we came straight enough when the horse was headed right, but we lost time.

ELIZABETH ELIZA: I am sorry enough I lost the exhibition, and seeing you take the diploma, Amanda. I never got the diploma myself. I came near it.

233

Mrs. Peterkin: Somehow, Elizabeth Eliza never succeeded. I think there was partiality about the promotions.

Elizabeth Eliza: I never was good about remembering things. I studied well enough but, when I came to say off my lesson, I couldn't think what it was. Yet I could have answered some of the other girls' questions.

Julia: It's odd how the other girls always have the easiest questions.

Elizabeth Eliza: I never could remember poetry. There was only one thing I could repeat.

Amanda: Oh, do let us have it now—and then we'll recite to you some of our exhibition pieces.

Elizabeth Eliza: I'll try.

Mrs. Peterkin: Yes, Elizabeth Eliza, do what you can to help entertain Amanda's friends.

Elizabeth Eliza: I'm trying to think what it is about. You all know it. You remember, Amanda—the name is rather long.

Amanda: It can't be Nebuchadnezzar, can it? That is one of the longest names I know.

Elizabeth Eliza: Oh, dear, no!

Julia: Perhaps it's Cleopatra.

Elizabeth Eliza: It does begin with a "C"—only he was a boy.

Amanda: That's a pity, for it might be "We Are Seven," only that is a girl. Some of them were boys.

Elizabeth Eliza: It begins about a boy—if I could only think where he was. I can't remember.

Amanda: Perhaps he "stood upon the burning deck"?

Elizabeth Eliza: That's just it—I knew he stood somewhere.

234

AMANDA: Casabianca! Now begin—go ahead!

ELIZABETH ELIZA: "The boy stood on the burning deck,"
When—when—
I can't think who stood there with him.

JULIA: If the deck was burning, it must have been on fire.
I guess the rest ran away, or jumped into boats.

AMANDA: That's just it.
"Whence all but him had fled."

ELIZABETH ELIZA: I think I can say it now.
"The boy stood on the burning deck,
Whence all but him had fled—"
[*Hesitates*] Then I think he went—

JULIA: Of course, he fled after the rest.

AMANDA: Dear, no! That's the point. He didn't.
"The flames rolled on, he would not go
Without his father's word."

ELIZABETH ELIZA: Oh, yes. Now I can say it.
"The boy stood on the burning deck,
Whence all but him had fled;
The flames rolled on, he would not go
Without his father's word."
But it used to rhyme. I don't know what has happened to it.

MRS. PETERKIN: Elizabeth Eliza is very particular about
the rhymes.

ELIZABETH ELIZA: It must be "without his father's head,"
or perhaps, "without his father said" he should.

JULIA: I think you must have omitted something.

AMANDA: She has left out ever so much!

MOTHER: Perhaps it's as well to omit some, for the ice-
cream has come, and you must all come down.

SOUND: *Voices and many footsteps.*

AMANDA: And here are the rest of the girls—and let us
all unite in a song!

Mystery

A Candle in the Mist

From *A Candle in the Mist,* by Florence Crannell Means. Published by Houghton Mifflin Co. Reproduced by permission of the publishers. Adapted for radio by Katherine Watson. (Grades 5-6)
30 minutes

Cast of Characters

JANEY GRANT .... fourteen-year-old girl

PA GRANT }
MA GRANT } .... Janey's parents

THAD GRANT .... Janey's twelve-year-old brother

LUCY GRANT .... Janey's baby sister

INGRID .... a servant girl

HAWKIN .... sixteen-year-old servant lad

INDIAN MAN

GRANDMOTHER

Sounds

Hammering with spoon
Footsteps
Scurry of feet
Bang of door
Door opening and closing

Indian voices
Barking of dogs
Blasts on horn
Pounding on dresser
Music

A Candle in the Mist

ANNOUNCER: The setting of "Candle in the Mist" is Wisconsin in the year 1871. The characters are Grandmother, Pa and Ma Grant. The Grants have three children: Janey, fourteen, her brother Thad, twelve, and Baby Lucy. Hawkin, a boy of sixteen and Ingrid, a much older woman, both escaped from the Indians at the time of the Sioux massacre and are now making their home with the Grants. It is Janey's birthday, and they are all sitting in the sunny Grant kitchen. Let's listen to their conversation—

THAD: Ma, can't Janey come out with Hawk and me and see how we've trained the little steers? She hadn't ought to wash dishes on her birthday.

LUCY: [*Hammering with spoon*] Me, too!

INGRID: Ay wash dishes. Mis' Grant, she got headache. She lay down.

PA: How does it feel to be fourteen, Daughtie? Like being an old lady?

LUCY: Janey putted away her dolly. In a wed dwess and white pinny. Way, way up in cupboard.

JANEY: Well, there wouldn't be anything left of her if I didn't, poor Angelica. Lucy ripped her seam this very day, to see what was inside; and Angelica lops over as if she had a headache. She lost so much stuffing. I hadn't played with her for ever so long.

PA: It's time you put away your doll-baby. You're big enough to cook and sew like your Ma. But what's this I hear about your wanting to go to Normal School? What idea have you got in your head, Daughtie?

239

JANEY: Well, Pa—well, you know girls do lots of things nowadays. What I'd like is to—to write poems and—and books.

PA: Worse and more of it. No money in it, Janey.

JANEY: I could teach school while I was getting started; but you don't get very good schools without Normal.

PA: [*Clearing his throat*] Janey, that's just what Ma and I have been threshing over. Money's scarce as hen's teeth, but we figure by close scrimping we can send you to Normal—send Thad off to school, too, when his time comes. That's your birthday present, that promise.

JANEY: Oh, Pa! Oh, Ma! Oh—

SOUND: *Footsteps approaching.*

MA: You young ones run along now. If Ingrid can manage, you go, too, Mother Grant, and get your nap.

SOUND: *Scurry of feet and bang of door.*

INGRID: Ay spose Hawkin don't get away to no schule.

PA: [*Impatiently*] We'll do what we can for Hawkin, Ingrid, but—

VOICE: [*Calling from distance outside*] Matt! Matt Grant!

PA: Sounds like Sam Sneed. Guess I'd better go and see what he wants.

SOUND: *Heavy footsteps and door slams.*

INGRID: Don't care. Hawkin better boy dan T'ad or Yaney eider.

MA: I feel bad about Hawkin, myself. But he'll make his way, Ingrid.

SOUND: *Door opening and closing. Footsteps.*

PA: Ma! Oh, Ma!

MA: Yes, Matthew?

PA: Look at this! Just look at this!

MA: Why, whatever have you got?

PA: Money! Money enough to choke a cow!

MA: But I don't understand—

PA: Sam Sneed brought it over. Seems they've got Brother Walter's estate settled. He left $4,000 to fix up the church wall and belfry; and being I'm treasurer, Sam brought it over so I could bank it. He ought to know good and well that I can't take the time to hyper off to Columbus, when the wheat's to be got in.

MA: But, Pa, you'll have to go. I'm scared to have it here, all that wad of money.

PA: Now, Ma, I don't dare risk the wheat. Here it is. You can think up a good safe place to hide it till Monday.

SOUND: *Footsteps fading out. Door slams.*

JANEY: Oh, Ma, whatever will you do with it?

MA: [*Falteringly*] I might put it in the feather bed—

JANEY: I've heard that's the first place a thief thinks of.

MA: Or in the rag-bag—

JANEY: They do say burglars always look in places like that. We might put it under the corn-meal in the bin —or in the teapot in the cupboard.

MA: If only I could think clearer. Such a dizzy headache.

SOUND: *Confusion of voices outside. Dogs barking.*

JANEY: Look, Ma! It's Indians going by.

LUCY: Looty thee, too!

JANEY: All right, Baby—Sister'll carry you. Only keep still as a mouse. We'll keep behind the lilac bush and watch them, but we mustn't let them see us.

SOUND: *Door opens and closes quietly—light footsteps. Indian noises continue.*

JANEY: [*Whispering*] Oh, Lucy, see, see what a dirty Indian girl! She's pretty, but, but—

LUCY: [*In high pitched voice*] 'Lo, 'ittle dirty dirl!

JANEY: Oh, Lucy, now you've done it. That old man— just like a monkey he looks—and he's stopping spang in front of us.

INDIAN MAN: Mebbe water?

JANEY: Ye-es. Right there's the windmill—and a cup hanging. Take all the water you want.

LUCY: Looty thcared of monkey man! Looty thcared!

JANEY: Hush, Baby. Just watch the little girl and the cute papoose. The minute we see they've shut the lane gate after them, we'll run tell Ma. I can't think why she didn't come to see them—but maybe she's been watching from the window. Of course Ingrid would hide if she saw them at all, she's so afraid of them. Thank goodness they've all had drinks now, and they're going.

SOUND: *Confusion of voices and barking dogs. Footsteps and opening and closing of door.*

JANEY: Ma, oh, Ma! Did you see them? Was it all right to—? Ma! Ma! What's wrong? Oh, Pa! Hawkin!

LUCY: Det up, Ma! Det up! Why Ma thleep on floor?

HAWKIN: Janey, did you call? I happened to be—why, Janey, Ma's fainted! Get a dipperful of water—ammonia. There! She's coming to. But you better blow the horn, Janey—your Pa ought to know. He's out at the barn.

SOUND: *Three blasts on horn.*

HAWKIN: Now, Janey, if you'll fix her bed, I'll carry her in there. She ought to be covered up and a hot flat iron put to her feet. Lucy, you go call your grandma, too, and Ingrid.

SOUND: *Door opening and closing—heavy footsteps.*

PA: [*Excitedly*] Why, Ma! What under the sun? What ever have you been up to? Janey, she doesn't look as if she knew me. Ma, it's Matt. That's right. Now you begin to look like yourself again.

SOUND: *Footsteps approaching.*

GRANDMOTHER: What's this? Mary sick?

PA: She must have fallen and hit her head. But she's going to be all right. You're a lot better, aren't you, Ma?

243

MA: [*Faintly*] Yes, some better.

GRANDMOTHER: Do get back to your work, Son. I can manage Mary.

PA: You think she's really all right, Mother? Well, then, I'll finish hitching up. I decided to go to Columbus this afternoon after all. I'll have to risk the wheat.

MA: [*Surprised*] You going to Columbus, Pa?

PA: Well, you were set on it, an hour ago. Uncommon set. So where's the money, Ma?

MA: The—money?

PA: The money. The church money. In the wallet. The four thousand dollars.

MA: Oh, Matthew, oh, surely you're joking. I don't remember anything about any church money.

PA: You don't remember anything about the money? About the four thousand dollars in the old wallet?

MA: Oh—bills in an old wallet—yes!

PA: Well, then, let's hear where you hid it, Ma.

MA: But—I don't know. It's as if the clouds closed in. I sat there holding it, and Janey heard the Indians, and then—

PA: Indians?

MA: [*Faintly*] Yes, a band of Indians came by. And then—I don't know. It's blotted out.

JANEY: Maybe you tucked it in your pocket, Ma? No, the pocket's empty. I don't believe you had time to go upstairs with it. I know! The teapot in the cupboard!

SOUND: *Footsteps.*

PA: Think, Mary, think! Could you have put it under the carpet? Or between the ticks? Thad, now that you've come in, you look around and see if you don't find an old wallet.

THAD: Is that all that's bothering you? Here it is, Pa, under this tipped-over chair by the dining-room cupboard.

PA: But it's empty—empty. Look here, is there anything else missing?

JANEY: There's nothing in the teapot, Pa. But—but Angelica's gone.

PA: [*Puzzled*] Angelica? Who's Angelica? You don't mean that doll-baby of yours? Good land, Janey, you don't think anybody's going to steal a doll-baby.

THAD: Janey, how was it dressed—your doll?

JANEY: Why, in a scarlet merino dress and a new white apron. Why do you ask, Thad?

THAD: I'll be hornswoggled if those Injuns ain't got it. A little Injun girl—I just saw them before I came in.

PA: Son, are you sure you aren't mistaken? China doll-babies are alike as peas in a pod.

THAD: No, sir, because I took note of that clean apron and the dirty little Injun.

PA: [*Pounding on the dresser*] Well, then, it's as plain as a pikestaff. Some one of those sneaking Indians came in and knocked Mary down and took off with the money. Grabbed the doll for his young one, I suppose.

MA: Lucy? Is Lucy here all right? Where's Lucy?

JANEY: She's all right, Ma. There she is now, coming over the stile. Lucy! Baby Lucy! Where have you been?

LUCY: Talkin to Injuns.

PA: It's a mercy the Indians didn't take her, too. Hawkin, you know some of their lingo. You come with me and we'll see if we can lay hands on that money.

JANEY: [*Faintly*] And my doll—

PA: [*Vehemently*] You don't think we'd go around hunting the doll-baby when four thousand dollars are gone?

LUCY: 'Ittle dirty dirl dot 'Gelica.

PA: Lucy! What are you saying. Did you see that doll-baby?

LUCY: Looty dave dolly to dirl. Dirl dot no dolly.

PA: [*With a great sigh*] You gave it to her? Then we're back where we started from. If the Indians didn't steal the doll, it's like enough they weren't in the house at all. And we've got no ground for searching them. But if they didn't take the money, then who did, for land's sakes?

HAWKIN: I might go and talk to the Injuns, Mr. Grant.

PA: [*Sharply*] I'd rather you'd stay on the place till this matter is cleared up, Hawkin.

HAWKIN: [*Slowly*] Those Indians are Sioux, sir. I'm always hoping I can learn something about my folks—

PA: For the present I wish you would stay here. You and Thad, come out to the field with me. We may as well get the wheat in. The womenfolks can be hunting for the money.

JANEY: Pa! Why, Pa! You can't think that Hawkin—

PA: We will not discuss the matter. Come, boys!

SOUND: *Footsteps receding. Door opening and closing. Silence for a few seconds.*

246

GRANDMOTHER: Janey, I keep hearing footsteps in the parlor, seems as though—

JANEY: I'll go see if there's anyone—

SOUND: *Opening and closing of door. Footsteps approaching.*

JANEY: Why, Hawkin! Didn't you go to the field with Pa and Thad? Why, Hawkin, you look so queer.

HAWKIN: Janey, your Pa thinks I'm mixed up in this money business.

JANEY: Oh, Hawkin, Pa speaks quick; but when he really thinks it out, he'll know you couldn't be.

HAWKIN: Like enough he'll make even *you* think it, Janey.

JANEY: No! Not ever! Not ever, Hawkin.

HAWKIN: If only I could believe that—why, it would be sort of like a candle set in the window—when everything is mist and blackness. Janey, here's something that belonged to my mother. It's just a plain little ring, but—would you—would you wear it until we see each other again?

JANEY: Of course, I'll wear it, Hawkin; but what do you mean, "until we see each other again"? Hawkin, you aren't going away?

HAWKIN: How could I stay, after—after this? I've got my other clothes and —

JANEY: Your little buckskin bag. Is that your Testament in it, Hawkin, stuffing it so full?

HAWKIN: Not my Testament, no. Forgive me, Janey, but this was something I had to take. I had to—I wanted it so bad. Oh, Janey, good-by! Good-by!

MUSIC: *Musical curtain.*

ANNOUNCER: We find the Grant family around the breakfast table this morning, as we hear Thad entering from the barn.

SOUND: *Door opening and closing—footsteps approaching.*

THAD: I'm as hungry as old Shep. Why—where is Hawkin?

PA: Yes, that's what I would like to know. It looked bad enough, his being the only one outside the family who knew about the money, but I was willing to give him the benefit of the doubt. But on top of that, though, he goes sneaking off to talk to those Indians without a word to me.

MA: Now, if it were you, Pa, would you feel like having much to do with a man that doubted you?

PA: Well, didn't I give him a home for four years?

MA: Hawkin earned his keep.

PA: Well, if it was I, I'd stay and prove myself clear. I'd not sneak off after dark.

MA: Yes, but you are a man grown. Hawkin is only a boy.

PA: But why would he run off if he hadn't anything to do with the money?

LUCY: Hawkie dot money. In a big bag.

JANEY: Hush, Baby. You don't know a thing about it.

LUCY: Do, too. Hawkin camed out of pa'lor. Janey sawed him. Looty sawed him, too.

PA: Jane, is there something you haven't seen fit to tell me?

JANEY: I—didn't think it was anything, Pa. It was last night. Hawkin came out of the parlor, but why shouldn't he?

PA: And what is this about the bag?

JANEY: He had his buckskin bag. Oh, Pa, Hawkin didn't —why he couldn't. I don't care if the bag did have something in it. I don't think it was as big as a roll of bills.

PA: And did he say anything?

LUCY: He cried—awmost. H-he s-said—

PA: What did he say, Jane?

JANEY: He said something about that he had to have it. He wanted it so bad. But—Pa, he didn't take the money. I know he didn't.

PA: There's no use wasting time. Better give his description to the sheriff.

MA: Pa—Pa, there's words that say "judge not." You're pretty quick to throw aside four honest years the minute circumstantial evidence turns up. It wouldn't be easy for a boy to live down a charge like that.

PA: Why didn't he make some attempt to clear himself?

GRANDMOTHER: Why don't you saddle Midnight and go off and hunt him yourself?

PA: I don't know but you've got the right of it there. Ma, you fix me a lunch and I'll be going.

MUSIC: *Musical curtain.*

ANNOUNCER: The sun is setting as Pa rides back from his search for Hawkin. After putting the horse in the barn, he enters the house.

PA: [*Tiredly*] Hello.

MA: Pa, you're tired. I'll fix you something to eat. You haven't had a bite since noon, have you?

PA: No, but I'll rest a while before I eat. I'm dog tired.

THAD: Did you find him, Pa?

PA: Of course I didn't find hide nor hair of him. I've looked the whole countryside over. Just now I've come from Columbus.

MA: Did you think you'd find trace of him in Columbus, Pa?

PA: No, I went to Columbus to get a loan from the bank to pay that church money back.

MA: And could you?

PA: No, I didn't get a loan. But I paid back every cent.

MA: But how?

PA: I've sold the place from under our feet. We haven't any home.

MA: [*Slowly*] Sold our home!

PA: There was nothing else to do. Banker Davis had a buyer.

MA: When must—we—?

PA: Give possession? Not until spring. Gives us time to look around. Janey, I guess you and Thad know this does away with any thoughts of your going to Normal School?

JANEY: Pa, that's—that's all right. Likely I couldn't ever learn to write books anyway.

MA: Now, Janey, don't say that. Show Pa the poem you wrote today. Maybe it will make him feel better.

JANEY: Here it is, Pa. [*Silence for a few seconds*].

PA: Why, Janey! Grandma, Ma, listen to this. Read it, Janey.

JANEY: I longed to be a star,
    Or else a flaming fire,
    That all men, near and far,
    Might marvel and admire.
    But God said, No, my child,
    Splendor is not for thee;
    I want you for my tallow dip,
    To burn for me.
    Burning in the wind,
    Burning in the dust,
    With a steadfast flame,
    Of belief and trust.
    Never letting doubt,
    Blow your clear flame out.
    Candle in the mist,
    Shining true and bright;
    Guiding wanderers home again,
    Through the stormy night.
    —Shine, little light, shine on,
    Till dark is lost in dawn.

GRANDMOTHER: It's very pretty. Did you copy it out of the *Advocate*?

PA: Why, Grandmother, our Janey wrote it. And I'm going to send it to the paper.

JANEY: Pa! You think they would really print it?

PA: You just wait and see if that editor doesn't snap it up before you can say Jack Robinson.

251

THAD: [*Teasingly*] Did you know it?
Janey is a poet.
Did you know it?
Janey is a poet.

MUSIC: *Musical curtain.*

ANNOUNCER: A year has gone by, a year filled with new experiences for the Grant family. They have driven across-country five hundred miles to the Government land in Minnesota; they have gone through a blizzard and a plague of grasshoppers. Janey has taught in the little district school and Pa has built the first frame house amid the soddies and log houses. Now the little town of Lucerne is to have its first community celebration, a big picnic dinner at Beaver Woods, a few miles away. Let's look in at the Grant house.

MA: There they are—four big pies. I'm glad I saved those cans of wild berries I put up last summer.

GRANDMOTHER: They do look nice. I'd give a pretty to help you get ready, but this old rheumatiz pins me to my chair. There's one good thing about it—it means a change of weather; and if we don't get rain pretty quick, there'll be fires springing up everywhere.

JANEY: Hadn't I better stay with you, Grandmother?

GRANDMOTHER: Stay home from the picnic? Not a mite of need. There's one thing I wish you could do, though, if there's time. I've set my heart on starting work on that wool dress of yours tomorrow. I can cut and baste even if my rheumatiz won't let me run the machine. Do you think you can dye the piece of goods for me, so it'll be ready?

JANEY: Of course I can, Grandmother. Haven't I watched you a hundred times?

GRANDMOTHER: Well, then, you use the clothes stick and don't get your hands in the dye. And you try a little of the indigo color while the washboiler's getting hot. Set that old kettle out on the ground so if you spill any it won't hurt. That's right. Now here's a piece of goods to test the color on. Dip it in and bring it back where I can look at it.

MA: You did a beautiful job of weaving, Mother. Janey will be proud of that dress.

JANEY: Here's the test-piece, Grandmother. Isn't it the loveliest color? I don't think there's anything prettier than blue.

LUCY: [*Loud wailing fading in*] Wanted boo dolly-dwess. Didn't want boo dolly.

JANEY: Will you look at what she's done this time!

MA: Oh, my baby.

JANEY: Your blue baby. Why, Lucy looks as if she'd fallen in all over! Look at her arms! And her hair!

GRANDMOTHER: Not a mite of use scrubbing. It'll have to wear off. As for her hair, you may as well cut it close to her head.

JANEY: She looks like a calico baby.

GRANDMOTHER: And that makes two Grants who stay home from the big doings.

MA: Three. I wouldn't think of leaving anything as busy as Lucy on your hands. I don't mind staying home, not a bit.

JANEY: I'll stay myself. I've had lots more outings than you, Ma. Besides, look at my hands.

PA: [*Calling from outside*] Mary, can you come right along? Our clock must've lost an hour. The wagons are all started for the picnic.

MA: Why, I'd feel so selfish—

JANEY: Here, Ma, I'll finish with Lucy. Get on your bonnet! Good-by.

SOUND: *Footsteps receding and door opening and closing.*

GRANDMOTHER: Janey, will you help me move over beside the south window? The sun will feel good to my old bones.

SOUND: *Janey's footsteps and Grandmother's lame shuffle.*

JANEY: There. Is that comfortable?

LUCY: [*Dolefully*] All the peoples gone!

JANEY: They do drop out of sight quick, over that north hill.

GRANDMOTHER: Janey! It almost seems as if I smell smoke!

JANEY: [*Sniffling*] Oh, Grandmother! Look, look! Out the east window. It's a prairie fire, just coming over the little ridge!

GRANDMOTHER: It can't cross Rock River—but there's our wheat—we'll send Lucy down to the village to see if there's anyone left to fight it. And you, Janey, you best hitch up the plough-horses and see if you can cut a firebreak—oh, thank goodness! I hear horses. The folks must have smelt the smoke and come back.

JANEY: But, Grandmother, they're coming from the wrong way.

GRANDMOTHER: They are, for a fact. Now who could it —Janey, it's a band of Indians!

JANEY: Oh, they're making a backfire! Grandmother, they're in time. They've saved our wheat.

LUCY: Pa and Ma are coming dwefful fast—and some Injuns, too.

JANEY: Why—one Indian—he's helping Ma—out of the wagon. They're—they're coming up the walk.

SOUND: *Opening and closing of door—many footsteps.*

JANEY: Hawkin! Oh, Hawkin! You've come back.

PA: You've surely lent a helping hand this day, you and your friends, Hawkin.

HAWKIN: We were lucky to be in time. The wind was our way, though, and we smelled the smoke a long way off, so we came at a gallop.

PA: Where were you and your friends bound for?

HAWKIN: Well, to tell the truth—here.

PA: But how did you learn that we were here?

HAWKIN: It was Janey's poem.

JANEY: My poem?

HAWKIN: I got a newspaper from the home place, and there it was—"A Candle in the Mist," by Jane E. Grant, Lucerne, Minnesota. A Candle in the Mist. And I thought, well, if Janey thinks like that, I'm coming back.

MA: Oh, Hawkin, boy, why did you ever leave us?

HAWKIN: There were two reasons, Mother Grant. It seemed as if I, for one thing, couldn't stay there any longer when Mr. Grant believed I took the money—couldn't stay when—anybody—believed I'd stolen something. Then I thought if I could find out if the Indians had taken your money—

JANEY: Oh, Hawkin, had they?

255

HAWKIN: Then you never did find it? No, Janey, they weren't that kind of Indians. Not this band. I knew that as soon as I saw old Weenonah—she was the chief's wife in the band Ingrid and I lived with. But I—investigated other matters. And here, Mr. Grant, sir, is a part of the sum.

INGRID: [*Wailingly*] Ay told you he ban gude boy. Oh, Hawkin, my Hawkin!

HAWKIN: Dear old Ingrid!

PA: [*Excited*] One hundred—two—three—Ma, here is six hundred dollars!

HAWKIN: Mr. Grant, you—don't still believe I had anything to do with your loss?

PA: Isn't it a logical thing to suppose, when you return a part of it?

JANEY: Oh, Pa—

PA: There, there, Janey. No, my boy, I don't believe you had anything to do with our loss—especially since the lost four thousand dollars was in fifties, and this six hundred is in fives and tens.

HAWKIN: I hoped maybe you wouldn't notice. I meant to get them changed, but there was no chance. But, sir, I would be glad if you'd take them. All the while I was trapping furs and selling them, I was thinking maybe it would help out.

PA: Thank you, my boy; but we'll make out. Keep it for your own schooling.

HAWKIN: And what about Janey's schooling? And, Janey, if I do go to school awhile, may I take your picture? I've kept it safe and sound.

JANEY: My picture?

HAWKIN: Why, yes, your daguerreotype in the little frame. You remember—you saw me with it in my buckskin bag, and said how full it looked. It wasn't just right to take the picture; but I had to have it, Janey. And you never thought wrong of me, never? Not even when things looked so awful bad?

JANEY: Of course not, Hawkin. When you really know a person, the way things look doesn't make any difference. Lucy's hair—it certainly looks blue, but I know it isn't.

HAWKIN: Like a candle in the mist. Janey, I've got something for you. Look! Here's your old doll.

JANEY: Why it's Angelica! Where did you ever—

PA: That doll-baby.

HAWKIN: It was at the Indian camp when I went there. I bought another doll for the little Indian girl who had it, so I could bring this one back to you.

JANEY: I'll wash up her clothes and put her in the cupboard where we can see her.

MA: Angelica—cupboard—

INGRID: Mees' Grant, what for you rip de stitches in doll's back, dat day? Tek clo's off and rip doll body where Yaney had sewed it up—

PA: What are you talking about, Ingrid? What day?

INGRID: Day de Inyins coming. She rip stitches—and den de Inyins comin' and Ingrid run hide.

MA: It's coming back to me. Janey, reach me the scissors. Let me rip that seam again—I climbed up to set her on the cupboard shelf, after I'd stuffed the roll of bills in her body—and then I was dizzy, and I must have fallen. Look, do look! The whole roll, $4000.

PA: The Lord be praised!

JANEY: And Hawkin, too!

LUCY: Me, too!

The Secret of the Rosewood Box

From *The Secret of the Rosewood Box,* by Helen F. Orton.
Published by J. B. Lippincott Company. Adapted for radio by William Ratigan and Katherine Watson, by permission of the publishers
and author.   (Grades 4-5)   30 minutes

CAST OF CHARACTERS

CHARLEY KING ⎫
⎬ .... children of ten or eleven
MABEL KING ⎭
FATHER ⎫
⎬ .... their parents
MOTHER ⎭
GRANDMOTHER KING
MAILMAN
MRS. NELSON .... a distant neighbor
LAURA MARTINEAU ⎫
⎬ ...... newly arrived school mates
ARTHUR MARTINEAU ⎭
MRS. MARTINEAU .... their mother

SOUNDS

Doorbell
Door opening
Door closing
Sound of envelope
being opened
Rustle of paper
Train whistle
Rumbling of wagon

Birds singing
Bear growling
Gun shots
Thunder storm
Rain on roof
Knocking on door
Music

The Secret of the Rosewood Box

ANNOUNCER: Once upon a time there was a family named King. They lived in a little village in New York State. There were Mr. and Mrs. King and Grandmother, and Charley and Mabel who were about ten years old. One day in March the doorbell rang—[*Fading*]

SOUND: *Doorbell.*

FATHER: Answer the door, Charley.

CHARLEY: Yes, Father. I'll see who it is. [*Fading*]

SOUND: *Door opening.*

CHARLEY: Why, it's the mailman!

MAILMAN: Hello, there, Charley! Say, give this to your father! I think it's that important letter he's been expecting!

CHARLEY: Golly, I hope so! Thanks!

MAILMAN: Don't mention it! So long!

CHARLEY: Good-by!

SOUND: *Door closing.*

CHARLEY: [*Fading in*] Dad! Dad! This must be that letter you've been waiting for!

FATHER: Let me see it! Hmmm!

SOUND: *Letter opening—rustle of paper.*

MABEL: Is the letter from Michigan, Daddy?

MOTHER: Now, Mabel! Let your father read his letter in peace!

MABEL: All right, Mother! I'm sorry.

GRANDMOTHER: Come sit on my lap, Mabel!

MABEL: Oh, Grandmother, I'm too big a girl to sit on anybody's lap! I'm going on eleven.

FATHER: Just listen to this! I have some important news! We're going to move! To Michigan!

CHORUS: Move? To Michigan? Way out West? Hurrah!

FATHER: Well, I'm glad all of you are pleased! This man is offering me one hundred acres of land very cheaply, and I think I'd better accept his offer!

CHARLEY: Oh! Will we have fun!

MOTHER: It's a journey of five hundred miles! How will we get there? In a covered wagon?

FATHER: Oh, no! We'll take the train most of the way and then take a wagon!

MABEL: That'll be fun! Won't it, Charley?

CHARLEY: I'll say! There are lots of deer and bears in the woods out in Michigan!

MOTHER: Will you go with us, Grandmother?

GRANDMOTHER: Of course I will! On one condition!

FATHER: And what is that, Grandmother?

GRANDMOTHER: That you let me take my rosewood bonnet box! There is something very valuable in it!

FATHER: Well, I don't know! We'll be very crowded! And that rosewood box might get lost!

CHARLEY: Don't worry, Dad! I'll look after it! I'll see that it gets there safely!

GRANDMOTHER: Thank you, Charley!

FATHER: Well, that settles it! We'll take the rosewood box along! Now all of you get your things packed! We'll leave for Michigan in about a week!

SOUND: *Musical curtain into train with whistle into musical curtain—out into wagon going slowly.*

CHARLEY: Boy! I'm glad we're off that train. How far is it to Michigan, Dad?

MOTHER: Why, Charley, we were in Michigan on the train.

FATHER: Of course we were! Why, we're almost home! Well, it's seventeen miles to the village of Hamlin; and from there it's about eight miles to our new home.

MOTHER: These roads are bumpy. We won't try to make it all in one day, will we?

FATHER: No, we'll spend the night in Hamlin.

GRANDMOTHER: Charley, are you taking care of my rosewood box?

CHARLEY: Yes, Grandmother. I have it tied on to one of the trunks with a piece of strong cord.

GRANDMOTHER: Oh, I'm so glad it's safe. These roads are very rocky! Where did you say it was?

CHARLEY: Why, right here on top of the—Jiminy crickets! It's gone!

GRANDMOTHER: Mercy me!

MOTHER: Oh, dear!

MABEL: Charley was just careless. He didn't tie it tight.

CHARLEY: I did, too. I tied it tight as could be.

FATHER: Whoa, boy, whoa, there.

SOUND: *Wagon stopping.*

FATHER: I watched Charley tie that bonnet box on and he did a good job. These roads are so bad the string must have broken.

CHARLEY: That's it, Dad. Here's part of the string still on the trunk.

MOTHER: It can't be very far back. Grandmother and Father and I will rest here while you and Mabel go back and look for it, Charley.

MABEL: That's fine. I'd like to go.

FATHER: But be careful! There might be animals in these woods.

CHARLEY: We'll be very careful, Dad. Come on, Mabel.

MUSIC: *Musical bridge.*

CHARLEY: It must have been right along here that it dropped off, Mabel.

MABEL: Yes—what's that in the road just ahead?

CHARLEY: Why, it's—it's the rosewood bonnet box. I'll go after it.

SOUND: *Growling of bear.*

MABEL: Look out, Charley. There's a bear in the bushes.

CHARLEY: Hurry up, Mabel! Run! It's a big black bear, too.

SOUND: *Gun shots.*

MABEL: What was that?

CHARLEY: Sounded like a gun. Hurry! Let's get away from here.

SOUND: *Gun shots and bear growl up to musical curtain out into birds.*

FATHER: Here come Charley and Mabel.

MOTHER: Running like deer.

GRANDMOTHER: Where is the rosewood box?

CHARLEY: [*Fading in*] I'm sorry, Grandmother. [*Panting*]

GRANDMOTHER: Didn't you find it?

CHARLEY: It's up there—up the road a ways— [*Panting*]

MABEL: But there's a bear too—and somebody shot at us —with a gun!

FATHER: Well, of all things! I'll take my gun and find out what this is all about.

CHARLEY: Take me with you!

FATHER: All right, but watch your step.

SOUND: *Musical curtain—into birds.*

CHARLEY: Here's where we found it, Dad.

FATHER: Are you sure?

CHARLEY: Yes, see the mark it left in the road.

FATHER: Well, it's certainly gone.

CHARLEY: Maybe the bear ate it up.

FATHER: No, I don't think bears like to eat rosewood bonnet boxes.

CHARLEY: Then maybe the man who fired the shots took it with him.

FATHER: Then we'll never see it again, I'm afraid. Come on, Charley. Let's get back to the wagon so we can be in our new home tomorrow.

CHARLEY: All right, Dad. But I'm going to find that box somehow. I promised Grandmother I'd watch it.

FATHER: There isn't much you can do now, son.

CHARLEY: I'll find a way. You'll see.

MUSIC: *Musical curtain.*

ANNOUNCER: Charley did his best to find the rosewood box, but he had no success at all. In the meantime, the King family had moved into their own home. Grandmother was unhappy because she had lost her rosewood bonnet box, and Mr. and Mrs. King were unhappy because the house was so small and they had no money to make it larger. One day, during a very bad thunderstorm, a lady named Mrs. Nelson stopped at the King home for shelter. She told about seeing a rosewood bonnet box—[*Fading*]

SOUND: *Thunder and rain on roof.*

CHARLEY: Where did you see it, Mrs. Nelson?

GRANDMOTHER: Yes, tell us! If we could only get that rosewood bonnet box back, all our troubles would be over.

CHARLEY: All *your* troubles would be, Grandmother. Mother and Dad would still be unhappy because this house is so small.

GRANDMOTHER: Maybe they would and maybe they wouldn't.

CHARLEY: What do you mean?

264

GRANDMOTHER: Never you mind, Charley. What were you going to say, Mrs. Nelson?

MRS. NELSON: Well, as I was saying, I saw that bonnet box one day last spring.

CHARLEY: Where?

MRS. NELSON: Back where I used to live—about fifteen miles the other side of the town of Hamlin.

GRANDMOTHER: That was my box all right.

MRS. NELSON: I imagine so. One day I saw a hunter go along our road with a gun over his shoulder and a box like that in one hand.

CHARLEY: That hunter must have been the one who fired the shots that Mabel and I heard.

GRANDMOTHER: But what happened to the box?

MRS. NELSON: Well, I don't rightly know, but I heard that the hunter exchanged the box for a dinner at the house down the road.

CHARLEY: Oh, that's easy then. Tell me the name of that family and I'll go there and get the box.

MRS. NELSON: I'm afraid it won't be as easy as that. The family moved away to a lumber camp, and they had such a funny name that I can't remember it.

CHARLEY: Jiminy crickets! It's like looking for a needle in a haystack, but I'll find that bonnet box yet.

MRS. NELSON: Oh, I remember. Her name is Mrs. Martineau.

CHARLEY: Mrs. Martineau! Well, that's a clue—just as they have in detective stories.

MRS. NELSON: You're not a bad little detective yourself. [*Pause*] The rain has stopped and I think I better be going.

CHARLEY: Good-by, ma'am—and thank you very much. I'll find that rosewood bonnet box yet.

MUSIC: *Musical curtain.*

ANNOUNCER: So Charley kept on looking for the lost rosewood bonnet box and a woman named Mrs. Martineau. But nobody by that name seemed to live in the neighborhood. However, more families moved out their way, and soon school was held in the home of a neighbor. One day as Charley was going home from school, he saw a little boy and a little girl lying on the grass. The girl was crying.

SOUND: *Birds—*

CHARLEY: What's the matter?

LAURA: [*Crying*] My brother, Arthur, stumbled over a big root and hurt his ankle and I can't get him home.

ARTHUR: She isn't big enough to carry me.

CHARLEY: That's too bad! But don't cry!

LAURA: [*Crying*] I'm not crying.

CHARLEY: What's your name?

LAURA: [*Crying*] Laura.

CHARLEY: Weren't you two in my sister's class at school this afternoon?

ARTHUR: Yes, this is our first day. We just moved out here.

CHARLEY: My name's Charley. Now don't worry and stop crying, Laura. I'll get you and your brother home.

SOUND: *Musical bridge—knocking on door.*

266

CHARLEY: I hope your mother's home.

LAURA: I'm sure she is.

ARTHUR: I hear her coming to the door now.

SOUND: *Door opening.*

MRS. MARTINEAU: Well, for goodness' sake! What's wrong with Arthur?

LAURA: He hurt his ankle, Mother. He can't walk very well.

MRS. MARTINEAU: Shut the door, Laura! I'd better look at it.

SOUND: *Door closing.*

ARTHUR: I'm all right, Mother.

MRS. MARTINEAU: We'll see. Just wait till I get this shoe and stocking off.

LAURA: Is it bad, Mother?

MRS. MARTINEAU: No, I don't think so. It's just a very slight sprain. I'll rub some liniment on it. Who's this young man?

LAURA: His name is Charley, Mother. He helped me bring Arthur home. I couldn't have done it myself.

MRS. MARTINEAU: Well, young man, I certainly appreciate what you've done for my boy and girl. The Martineaus will always be grateful.

CHARLEY: Martineau? Is your name Mrs. Martineau?

MRS. MARTINEAU: Why, yes! Is anything the matter? You're pale as a ghost.

CHARLEY: No, nothing's the matter. Everything's all right at last. At least I hope so. You must have my grandmother's rosewood bonnet box.

MRS. MARTINEAU: Indeed, I have. I've been trying to find the real owner for a long time. I never did think that hunter had any right to it.

CHARLEY: Can I have it back?

MRS. MARTINEAU: Indeed you can. Just as soon as I can get it from the closet.

MUSIC: *Musical curtain.*

MABEL: Here comes Charley now, Mother.

MOTHER: He's late tonight.

FATHER: He must have played after school.

MOTHER: Well, I can't blame him. This house is too small to play in.

FATHER: If we only had enough money to make it larger!

MOTHER: How much would it cost?

FATHER: About two hundred dollars. Just two hundred more than I have.

GRANDMOTHER: Oh, dear! And to think I lost that rosewood box.

FATHER: What's the rosewood box got to do with two hundred dollars?

GRANDMOTHER: Never you mind. I know what I know.

MABEL: Charley's carrying something. I can't see what it is. He's coming in.

SOUND: *Door opening.*

MABEL: Hello, Charley.

SOUND: *Door closing.*

268

MABEL: What's that under your arm?

CHARLEY: Hurrah! It's Grandmother's rosewood box.

FATHER: Where did you find it?

MOTHER: How in the world?

GRANDMOTHER: Questions can come later. Let me see my box, Charley!

CHARLEY: Here it is, Grandmother. I told you I'd bring it back to you.

GRANDMOTHER: So you did. Please hand me that tack lifter, Charley.

FATHER: Here it is.

MABEL: What are you going to do, Grandmother?

MOTHER: Why, Grandmother—that's no way to act. Just think of the trouble Charley had finding that box for you. Don't pull the tacks out and rip out the lining.

GRANDMOTHER: I know what I'm doing. There. See what's under the lining.

MOTHER: Why, it's money!

FATHER: Lots of money.

CHARLEY: Jiminy crickets!

GRANDMOTHER: Yes, here they are. Ten twenty-dollar bills.

MOTHER: Two hundred dollars!

FATHER: Why, that's just what we need to make this house larger.

GRANDMOTHER: Yes, that's the secret of the rosewood box.

MUSIC: *Musical curtain.*

Buckaroo

From the story, *Buckaroo*, by Fjeril Hess. Published by the Macmillan Company. Reproduced by permission of the publishers and the author. Adapted for radio by Toni Hult.   (Grades 6-7)
30 minutes

CAST OF CHARACTERS

LYNN .... city-bred college girl
TED NORTON .... cowboy son of Ma Norton
MA NORTON .... president of the School Board
DAN .... her twenty-two-year-old son
JASPER .... her thirteen-year-old son
DOROTHY .... her twelve-year-old daughter

SOUNDS

Window opening
Tramping and lowing
  of cattle
Crack of whip
Dog barking
Dog whining
Gallop of horse
Footsteps
Weeping

Horses' hoofbeats
Cracking of ladder
Crackling twig
Thump of falling
  ladder
Rocks tossed on table
Jingle of chains
Tearing of paper
Music

Buckaroo

ANNOUNCER: Good afternoon, boys and girls. Today we
have a radio drama, *Buckaroo*. What boy or girl
wouldn't like to be a buckaroo and ride the range?
It's a free life—fresh air and golden sunshine—and no
one telling you just what to do. No wonder Lynn Garrow, a city-bred girl, after many months of steady
grinding college work is excited; for she is re-reading
the letter from the president of the school board of
Piñon School Number Nine, Big Smoky Valley, Nevada—three thousand miles from her home in New
York City—

LYNN: [*Reading*] Smoky Valley, Nevada. To the Teachers' Agency: I like this girl's photographs. *She means
me.* Send her along, please. She looks like a smart
girl, though rather young. Is she good at figures?
We've got a bunch of buckaroos on this ranch who say
they'd like a little high school work in the evenings.
We aim to take good care of our school marms; so
this one can tell her folks we've got lots of gentled
horses on the place, and not to worry about snake bites.
It's a nice country up here; some of us have been living
here quite a spell, in other words, all our lives.
    Carburetor Ike will meet the young lady in Tono-
pah and bring her in to us. Just let us know when she
is coming so Ike can be there. She can't mistake him,
for he's the homeliest man in Nevada. Respectfully
yours, J. R. Norton, President of Directors, Piñon
School District.

ANNOUNCER: The first night in Nevada, Lynn Garrow
stayed at the one and only hotel in Tonopah, forty
miles from the ranch. Early the next morning she was

274

awakened by a noise. She rushed to the window where her dog Nip lay sunning himself in an Indian basket.

SOUND: *Window opening—fade in tramping and lowing of cattle.*

ANNOUNCER: As far as the eye could see, the street was filled with cattle, rubbing shoulders, pushing, heaving along in a dense mass. Their backs and shoulders, moving so close together, gave an illusion of muddy water tumbling headlong down its course. Now and then one of the men would crack his twenty-four foot whip over the tail of some loitering steer.

SOUND: *Sharp crack of whip. Dog barking.*

LYNN: Here, Nippy. I'll hold you up so you can see the cattle.

SOUND: *Dog whines and barks excitedly.*

LYNN: Oh, Nip, I can hardly wait to start for Big Smoky where I can try my hand at riding the range. Oh! I knocked your basket off the ledge. Help! My basket! Somebody rescue it!

SOUND: *Gallop of horse.*

LYNN: Oh, there's a tall, good-looking buckaroo pushing his horse up on the high sidewalk.

TED: [*Fading in*] Drop this basket, Ma'am?

LYNN: Oh, thank you. I was afraid your cattle would trample it.

TED: You're welcome, Ma'am. Pleased to meet you.

LYNN: Oh, er—er—thank you again. Nip wouldn't have a very comfortable ride up to Piñon School had he lost his bed.

TED: Piñon School! [*Excitedly*] Did you say Piñon School? Well, if Ole Lady Luck ain't with us! Ole Lady Luck! [*Fading out*]

ANNOUNCER: When Lynn Garrow reached Big Smoky Valley that evening, the unpainted ranch house with blinds askew looked desolate and ugly. Rambling corrals and barns made of willows, branches and mud lay beyond in the shadow of late afternoon. The ranch yard was cluttered untidily with machinery, cans and chickens.

SOUND: *Dogs barking.*

ANNOUNCER: Two dogs rushed out, barking fiercely. Lynn's spirits drooped. New York seemed a long way off. Big Smoky Valley with its barren length and breadth seemed overpowering. She swallowed the lump in her throat and braced herself to meet J. R. Norton and his buckaroos.

MA NORTON: Howdy, Miss Garrow. I'm J. R. Norton and President of the School Board.

LYNN: How do you do, Mrs. Norton. You're—President of the Board! I expected J. R. Norton to be a man.

MA NORTON: And this is my son Daniel. He's twenty-two.

LYNN: How do you do, Daniel.

DAN: Howdy, Miss Garrow.

MA NORTON: And this is Jasper. He's thirteen and a trapper.

LYNN: How do you do, Jasper.

276

JASPER: Howdy, Miss Garrow.

MA NORTON: And Dorothy's twelve, the baby of the family. And Ted's off to a rodeo. He's my eldest.

DAN: Glad you got here all right. You'll soon know all of us.

MUSIC: *Musical curtain.*

ANNOUNCER: In her desolate bedroom, Lynn whispered to her reflection in the mirror—

LYNN: [*Whispering*] Brace up, old lady. Don't let anybody guess that Nevada, so far, looks like the end of the world.

ANNOUNCER: For supper that evening there was a platter of large sardines swimming in mustard sauce, boiled potatoes, bread and butter, and milk in which clots of cream bobbed up and down. The room was close and warm; and through the open kitchen door swarms of flies entered, settling at will on the table. Lynn remembered the dainty dinner table at home and ate almost nothing. She was glad to escape to the out-of-doors. We hear Dorothy say—

DOROTHY: See those lights—fifteen miles away. That's Round Top, where we get our mail. Dannie goes to town *every* Saturday!

LYNN: [*Despairingly*] You get mail—*once* a week.

DOROTHY: [*Proudly*] You bet! When it's good weather, we do.

LYNN: [*Whispering*] When it's good weather—mail *once* a week. [*Fading out*]

ANNOUNCER: Early next morning Lynn went out for a walk. A small stream ran through the ranch yard near the house; and across this stream, Lynn saw a tiny

277

half-built house of willow, brushes and mud, perhaps nine by thirteen. She crossed over to explore.

DAN: Morning, Miss Garrow.

LYNN: Oh, good morning, Danny.

DAN: I see you've been looking over your schoolhouse already.

LYNN: My schoolhouse? You mean—this is Piñon School, District Number Nine?

DAN: Yes, sir. Piñon School District Number Nine. We ought to get that temple of learning finished tomorrow. Soon's Ted gets home, you'll see the mud fly.

LYNN: Piñon School Number Nine. [*Whispering*] Buck up, old girl, and make the best of it.

DAN: If I had help, I could finish them walls today.

LYNN: Let me help you! I'd love to be a carpenter's assistant.

DAN: Fine! The gang will gather in half an hour in front of the People's University. Bring your overalls but leave your manicures at home.

MUSIC: *Bridge.*

LYNN: Well, after all this work I know I'll have a good appetite tonight.

DAN: We can't do any more on the schoolhouse, Ma, until Ted comes. We got the walls done, but he'll have to help with the roof.

MA NORTON: I think mebbe Ted'll come tonight, Danny, but I wish you'd go take a look at his horse in the round corral. He don't seem to look right to me, and I'm afraid he is dying.

278

SOUND: *Footsteps receding.*

DOROTHY: Oh, Miss Garrow, Ted's horse must've eaten moldy hay or something that caused bloat. Oh, I hope he doesn't die. It would break Ted's heart.

SOUND: *Weeping and footsteps approaching.*

DOROTHY: Oh, Danny, you're crying. The horse *is* dead. Oh, poor Ted!

LYNN: [*Weeping*] I feel so very sorry.

DAN: If Ted comes home tonight, don't anybody tell him. Come on, let's take a ride and see if we can't cheer up a little. I can tell him tomorrow.

MUSIC: *Bridge.*

SOUND: *Horses' hoofbeats.*

JASPER: Sh! Stop! Look!

ALL: What is it, Jasper?

JASPER: [*Whispering*] There's the Blue again. I told you I'd seen him up here last week.

DAN: I got to capture that horse or bust a leg. I'll ride up on the ridge and try to get back of him. Jasper, you ride on ahead and try to head him off. You girls yell like blazes if the Blue comes this way.

LYNN: Blue? Why do you call him the Blue?

DOROTHY: He's a wild horse that Danny discovered last year and has been chasing ever since. He's bound to catch him because he is such a beautiful horse. Look! Look!

279

LYNN: Oh, I see him. He's staring at us with his ears pointed forward. That heavy forelock flung over his eyes certainly gives him a wild look.

SOUND: *Horse running.*

DAN: [*Disgusted*] Missed him again!

JASPER: Whoopee! He got away!

DOROTHY: If Ted had been here, I bet he would have roped him.

SOUND: *Hoofbeats of horse approaching.*

TED: [*Fading in*] Hi ya, Buckaroos!

ALL: Ted!

DAN: Miss Garrow, meet my big ornery brother, Ted.

TED: How are you, Miss Garrow?

LYNN: Why, you're that brown-faced cowboy who rescued my basket from the sidewalk in Tonopah.

MUSIC: *Musical curtain.*

LYNN: Monday! My first day in Piñon School, District Number Nine. I want this year to be one that my youngsters will look back on with a sort of surprise to think that it was school at all. I really don't know what I mean by that, but this has to be fun for all of us, and not just a grade to be covered.

ANNOUNCER: Lynn Garrow was dead tired at the end of the first day of school. She was glad of the opportunity to get out in the open when Dorothy said—

DOROTHY: Come on, Teacher, let's get our horses and ride over to Black Canyon. I'll show you a gold mine Ted has over there.

LYNN: A gold mine! All right, Dorothy. [*Whistles*]
Come on, Nip.

SOUND: *Barking.*

DOROTHY: Let's not stop to saddle. Black Canyon isn't
far and it's fun to ride Indian-fashion.

SOUND: *Gallop of horses.*

LYNN and DOROTHY: Yippeee-ee! [*Laughing*]

MUSIC: *Bridge.*

ANNOUNCER: The girls tied their horses to a tree. They
crept along a narrow ledge of rock to a flat shelf on
the side of the hill and looked down into a dim hole
about three feet across. Down one side was a ladder,
warped by rain and bleached by sun. The end of the
ladder was only dimly visible thirty feet below.

DOROTHY: There's a tunnel down there where the ladder
ends. It runs back into the mountain about fifty feet.
Ted took me down once when he was working on it.

LYNN: Does Ted work here now?

DOROTHY: No, only once a year. You have to do so much
work a year on a claim in order to hang on to it, and
he usually does his in the spring when ranching is
slack.

LYNN: I'd climb down there if it weren't so dark. The
ladder seems strong enough.

DOROTHY: There are some candles down there in a tin box
behind the foot of the ladder, and maybe some matches.

SOUND: *Nip whines.*

Lynn: All right, Nip, old thing, want to go along? Down you go with me. The ladder seems perfectly sound. [*Fading out*]

Sound: *Cracking of ladder.*

Dorothy: Oh, Miss Garrow. The ladder—one side's cracking! Come back quick, before something else breaks!

Lynn: I can't. If I didn't have Nip I might make it, but I don't dare let go of him.

Dorothy: The ladder! It's jiggling!

Sound: *Nip whines.*

Lynn: I'm going on down, Dorothy. I can't hold Nip any longer. Go and get my rope from the saddle and haul him up on it. I'll get back somehow if this one timber will hold.

Sound: *Nip whines.*

Dorothy: O.K.

Lynn: I'll step lightly. [*Crackling sound*] Oh, it's giving way. Listen, Nip, I'll reach down as far as I can, and then I'll have to drop you.

Sound: *Fall of ladder, girl and dog.*

Lynn: Ugh! Ugh! We landed in a heap. Ugh! Guess I'm all right. Just a few scratches and bruises.

Sound: *Nip whines.*

Dorothy: [*Off*] Hey, Miss Garrow, don't you remember? We rode over bareback, and so there's no rope. I'm going home to get the boys. [*Fading out*]

SOUND: *Nip whines.*

LYNN: Oh, dear! Well, Nip, we might as well explore the tunnel just to pass the time away. Boy, it's dark in here. Careful! Don't stumble over all that fallen rock. Ted must've done considerable prospecting. Might as well take samples. I'll just fill my pockets full of rocks. Oh, here are some better specimens—all gold!

BOYS: [*Off*] Hey! Miss Garrow! Hey!

MUSIC: *Bridge.*

ANNOUNCER: She meant to empty her pockets of those dull colored rocks, but in her excitement she forgot to do so. In a short time the boys succeeded in rescuing both girl and dog. Later at the supper table she remembered her samples.

LYNN: Take a look at this, everybody.

TED: Fool's gold! [*Laughter*]

LYNN: No!

TED: Honest! Fool's gold! [*Laughter*]

SOUND: *Rocks tossed on table.*

LYNN: Then these old rocks aren't any good either.

TED: Here! Let's see that. Say! Looks like you got something there. We'll just send that away to be assayed. And now that you have proven yourself such a real buckaroo, how would you like to go on a deer hunt?

MUSIC: *Bridge.*

SOUND: *Horses racing, whirling romals, spur chains jangling.*

283

JASPER: Yahoo! [*Laughter*]

ALL: Yahoo! We're off! [*Laughter*]

ANNOUNCER: On they rode, like mad, romals whirling, spur chains jangling. Dannie pulled up as suddenly as he had started; and the four found themselves bunched together, panting and laughing. [*Laughter.*]

DAN: Say! We're really climbing now. Sh! Deer tracks. Follow me.

TED: [*Excitedly*] Look, Dannie, there's the Blue again!

ANNOUNCER: There, directly ahead in a tiny clearing, stood the Blue quietly feeding. Dan unbuckled his rope and handed Ted one end of it, which he would pass around a tree after Dan had thrown the horse. He waved Jasper off to the left. Dan then stole forward to the edge of the trees bordering the clearing. Lynn wished he'd give Ted the rope, for he was more expert. But she knew Dan would rather lose the horse than not catch him himself.

DAN: [*Whispering excitedly*] For the Blue—to raise his head. Ted, step on a twig!

SOUND: *Twig crackling.*

ANNOUNCER: The Blue flung up his head, whirling at the same time. A flash in the sun, and the rawhide sang in the air. The still mountain air was split by a wild frightened whinny. And the Blue was caught.

DAN: [*Coaxing*] Whoa, boy. Whoa, there. The rope, Ted. A little more slack! Whoa! Easy, whoa! You can't get away. My, but you're a beauty! Too proud to kick and fight. Now let me pat you on the nose. You would like to fight your way to freedom, wouldn't **you?**

TED: Doggone. We forgot the deer hunt. And here I promised Ma a venison steak for breakfast. [*Fading out*]

MUSIC: *Musical curtain.*

ANNOUNCER: Then, shortly before Christmas—of all times —the whole family came down with flu, one at a time; but Christmas day found them all stirring around again. Each member selected a chair or a cushion on the floor near the tree and piled up his gifts, as Ted and Dannie read off the names on the packages. Lynn appreciated most the hand-wrought silver spurs, which were the gift of Ted and Dannie.

DAN: The one for the right foot's from me, so's you can scratch harder with it. [*Laughter*]

TED: Well, I guess that is the last present.

MA NORTON: Wait! What's that white envelope there in the tree?

TED: Why, sure enough. And it's for you, Ma.

MA NORTON: Thanks.

SOUND: *Tearing of envelope.*

ALL: Read it, Ma. Read it out loud.

MA NORTON: Merry Christmas from Ted and the Broken Ladder Mine—one half interest in said mine leased on contract to the Golden Slipper Company, Incorporated —for the first year at guarantee of ten thousand dollars. Ted! Ted!

DAN: Broken Ladder Mine. Yippee, Ted!

MA NORTON: We sure owe you a lot, Miss Garrow, for falling down the ladder.

LYNN: Mercy! Don't give me any credit. Broken Ladder Gold Mine. It's a grand name.

285